PART 1

FINDING MY VOICE

Chapter 1

1737

My cheeks are on fire. Oldest Sister's jokes are always at my expense, although I don't understand this one. She and her two sisters are laughing hard.

"Sancho it is!" exclaims Youngest Sister. "Charles Ignatius Sancho. Hmm, it has an educated ring to it!"

This sets them off again. I can see right to the back of Oldest Sister's mouth where her breakfast is. I try not to look and busy myself at the side table cutting slices of seed cake, ready to offer them some more.

These three ladies are not *my* sisters but sisters to each other. They think of me as their pet, their property, but I'm not. I'm me. I was given to them when I was two years old so they, and this house here in Greenwich, are all I know. All that I can remember, anyway. Just lately they have not been as nice to me as they used to be. I've been trying to think why they don't seem to like me much any more, as I don't think I have changed, except for the fact that I am getting taller. I don't want to ask why they're laughing, but as it seems to be at me, I feel I must.

"What's so funny about you choosing 'Sancho' for my surname?"

"Why, he is a character in a famous book," says Oldest Sister.

This makes me feel a little better, sort of special in a way.

"Over here, Boy," Youngest Sister says. I take the seed cake over to her.

There is something about the way they are still laughing that makes me want to know more.

"What book?" I ask. "And who is he?"

"He was the servant of Don Quixote," Youngest Sister says, putting a slice of cake straight into her mouth and picking up a second which she drops on to her plate.

"A very stupid servant. One that could not read or write. So it's a perfect name for you, don't you think?" Middle Sister is speaking. She always follows whichever is the last of her sisters to speak.

This is too much for me. "But I want to learn! I've been asking for ages. It's you who won't let me," I blurt out.

Usually, I am much more careful about how I speak to them and always attach a smile. I'm eight now and I have learned over many years of working for them to make a pleasant face, however I feel on the inside.

"A servant has no business reading – or writing, for that matter. Whatever next! Do you want to become a lawyer?" Oldest Sister says. It's her turn now to help herself from the plate I am holding out. She always has the sharpest tongue.

This makes them laugh again but I am not put off that easily.

"Please Madam, I want to learn about the world and read about what other people are thinking. Maybe even …" I hesitate.

"What? Write down what *you* think?"

I nod.

"No one wants to know what a silly young Black boy thinks. Good heavens! 'I had porridge for breakfast today, it was lumpy. Last night I had soup, it was lumpy too.' No, no, no! You will become bad at the only thing you are good for, which is to do our bidding."

I turn away from her, my eyes filling up with tears. I don't want to let any of them see how hurtful her words are. But I am not ready to give up just yet. Being able to read and write is my deepest wish.

Back at the side table, I put the plate down and cover it.

"I-I-I could read your shopping lists and not forget

anything ever again. I could learn some poems and entertain you with them. I could—"

"Read the newspapers? Become a Member of Parliament? Vote? I'd rather see you back in the West Indies. How would you like to plant cane on a sugar plantation and get flogged instead of live in a lovely house in Greenwich? Don't think we wouldn't put you on a boat and send you there."

There is a snarl now in Oldest Sister's voice. Quickly I give a little laugh, as though I know learning to read and write is a silly idea. Her temper gets violent sometimes.

My laugh works and she changes the subject. "Have you cleaned the grates upstairs?"

I shake my head. "No, Madam," I say, eager to leave the room.

"Well, Master Sancho, you'd better be up there before I can reach that broom to brush your woolly head. It looks like it needs a clout."

The sisters laugh again as I make my escape. It's no good. No matter how hard I try, they are never going to agree to me learning to read and write. They are not the type to change their minds, even though it needn't cost them a penny as I'm sure I could teach myself.

Upstairs in Oldest Sister's bedroom I bend down and start clearing the ashes from the fire I banked up overnight. It's gone out now and the grate is cold. Often, I make up tunes to keep my spirits up while I'm working, but this morning it feels especially difficult. I squeeze out a couple of notes, which sound pitiful. I know there are lots of little boys and girls worse off than me, some are sent to work climbing up chimneys and going down mines.

Why *are* the sisters being so mean to me? I do my best every day, but nothing seems to please them. I try to hum again. I like Vivaldi and think back to a concert they took me to when I was very small. I suspect the tune I'm humming doesn't sound like Vivaldi at all, but that makes me smile. I don't care, this tune is mine. I made it up. My humming gets bolder as I sweep the cold grey ashes from under the grate. I tiptoe quietly to the door and listen. I can hear the sisters talking downstairs in the kitchen with Cook and, satisfied that I will be on my own for a few minutes at least, I return to the fireplace.

I spread out the ashes so they make a thin rectangle and, using my finger, make an "A" and then an "a". I have to think hard about how to make the shapes. Next to them I draw out "B" and "b". Unknown to the sisters, I already know my alphabet, only I'm not going to tell them.

It happened like this. All three sisters have embroidery samplers hanging in their bedrooms, made up of beautifully coloured letters, which they sewed when they were young children themselves. The alphabet was under my nose for years, only I didn't know it! One morning, Oldest Sister left a book open by her bedside and I looked at the pages when I was sweeping. Then I happened to glance up at the sampler above her bed before turning back to the book. The marks were the same! I realized these were the tools I needed to learn for reading and writing! Ever since then I have been committing the marks to memory. There are twenty-six of them, and each has a big and a small version that look a bit different. Each day, as I clean out the grates from the fireplaces, I spread out cold ashes with the brush and use my finger to draw a letter "A" and "a" – the samplers connect both to each other – or I practise another letter. I can't spend too long as I don't want the sisters to know. So far, none of them have noticed the lesson hanging on the walls in their bedrooms and I don't want them to.

I begin to copy the letters at the bottom of Oldest Sister's sampler. "Home Sweet Ho—"

"Sancho!"

The shout comes from Middle Sister, who I hear begin to climb the stairs. I sweep up the ashes quickly before she can see.

"Still doing the grates? Slowcoach! Leave that for now. Cook needs you to go to market."

"Yes, Madam," I say, relieved not to have been discovered.

I walk down the street, basket in hand, with the shopping list in my head. All around me I see shop signs – some with symbols, like the red and white stripes for the barber and the pawnbroker's three golden spheres, but some with letters over their doors. One day, I promise myself, I shall be able to read all the shop signs and more.

On the way home I am still thinking about this morning's conversation. I have never had a surname, and nobody has ever called me Charles, which is my first name. Only Ignatius, or "Boy". I decide I like the name Sancho. I feel sure the Sancho from the book the sisters mentioned was a nice person, just like me, even if he could not read or write. I'm sure if Don Quixote's Sancho had the chance and wanted to enough, he could have learned his alphabet too. If I get the chance, I shall learn it for both of us, and for every child who does not have the opportunity. I shall take the name of Sancho and be proud of it.

The garden gate creaks loudly as I lift the latch. It does the same when I close it behind me. I hope that one day soon I will be able to write my name. I have already made a start, by learning to draw the letters of the alphabet. The only problem, and I'm not quite sure how to get over it, is I don't know what sounds these letters make.

Chapter 2

A little later in the spring, when tender leaves unfurl and blossom decks the trees, I walk to Blackheath Common to watch the quarry men. I've got some time off at last.

The quarrymen are digging. It's a rowdy business with carts jostling each other and men shouting as they shovel gravel, sand and chalk on to a cart before heading off to the river. Here, it's loaded on to boats to take for use in all the building work that's going on around London. The birds singing in the beautiful blossom trees are sweet-sounding and the shouts of the men working in the quarry are jerky and jarring. I like to hear the two worlds clashing. It makes me feel alive.

When I've seen enough, I turn away and find a quiet spot to be by myself. It hasn't rained for a few days and the sun feels warm. Winter has passed and I look forward to longer days and fewer layers of clothing to struggle with. The walk here from Greenwich is not too far, and never tires me, but the walk back is different. I have to drag myself back to the house.

When I was very small the sisters used to bring me to Blackheath Common in an open carriage. I loved those trips. Before we left the house, they dressed me up in fine clothes and wrapped my head with a silk cloth, held in place with a ruby red brooch. I sat beside them in the carriage and waved at passers-by who stopped to stare. I think the sisters liked me then.

A stout stick at my feet makes me pick it up. The earth is bare so I brush away the leaves and bits of grass that have settled on it. I pause before starting to draw a very large "D". I begin with the straight up and down line. I've gone around the first corner at the top and am finishing the second corner at the bottom, turning back to join it to the straight line, when I break into a skipping dance around the stick. I'm tired of being stuck in the house and it feels good to stretch my legs.

A man on horseback is looking at me. I drop the stick and take off my shabby felt hat to make a low bow. It is a rather fancy bow because, firstly, he is on a horse and, secondly, his tricorn hat with its navy-and-white rosette looks a lot grander than mine and, thirdly, the spring sunshine has put me in a very happy mood.

The man nods and touches his hat as he turns to go

but then he changes his mind, digs his heels into the horse's flank and ambles over. The horse gets a lot bigger as it approaches and I begin to feel nervous. Have I been rude? Is he going to take me back to the sisters and make a complaint? The man looks down, and cocks his head to one side. He dismounts, letting go of the horse's reins. It immediately lowers its head and starts to munch the grass.

"What letter is that, young man?"

I feel relief, and then shame.

"I-I-I don't know how it sounds, Sir."

"Don't you now. Well, it's a very sturdy 'D' and the sound is 'duh'."

"Yes, Sir."

"Say it, go on."

"Duh, Sir," I say, and give a little bow, putting one hand behind my back and the other across my waist as I lower my head and bend forward slightly. I take a sidelong look at the "D" to make sure I remember the sound that goes with it. This is a marvellous beginning!

"Very good." He studies me for a moment before saying, "Shall we play a game? I'm going to make some more letters and you can copy them."

I am astonished. "Yes, Sir," I say, forgetting to bow this time and grinning instead.

The man searches about and I pick up my stick quickly and give it to him before he changes his mind. He grasps it firmly and makes an equally large circle to go with my "D" and makes its sound. After that, he draws the letter "G" – which I always find hard to do – and makes its sound too. He asks me to repeat the sounds after him. I like this game, so long as there are not too many sounds at once.

"Tell me what they are again."

"Yes, Sir," I say. I smile but my bottom lip trembles slightly as I'm afraid I've got it wrong. He seems used to giving orders that must be obeyed and his horse is very big, stamping the grass and snorting steam through its nostrils right beside me.

"Take your time," the man says kindly. "It's quite a hard thing I'm asking you to do."

I stare at the letters.

"Duh," I stumble out.

"Bravo. Make each of the sounds, please, in turn."

"Duh – oh – and, erm – guh."

"Good. And run the sounds together."

"Duh – oh – guh, duh-oh-guh, do-g, dog. Dog? *Dog?* Is it, Sir? Does it really say dog?"

"It does. Well done, my boy." The man is smiling.

I run around in circles. "It says 'dog', it says 'dog'. My first word. I read my first word!" I throw my arms around the man's legs and crush them to me before letting go. The horse stamps and whinnies, which brings me to my senses.

"Sorry, Sir, it's just that I'm excited!" I make a deep bow this time, looking sideways at his horse.

When I come up the man is looking at me thoughtfully. "What is your name, young man?"

"Ignatius ... Sancho, Sir." My new name feels strange on my tongue, but I like how it sounds.

"And where do you live, young Master Sancho?"

"I live in Greenwich, Sir, with—"

Suddenly my face drops.

"What's the matter?"

"I can't tell you where I live, Sir, beg your pardon. They don't want me reading and writing. I will get into trouble, please don't tell."

"Don't worry, Ignatius, I won't tell. It can be our secret for the moment. I live over there." The man points to a grand house across the park. "Next time you are free, whenever you want, knock on the side door. I will instruct my butler to let you in and you will say that the Duke of Montagu asked you to call on him."

"The d-d-duke?" I stammer.

"Yes. I am the Duke of Montagu and pleased to meet you. I have long thought that the only difference between an educated man and an unschooled one is that of opportunity, or lack of opportunity. You may use my library, look at the books and the maps. Would you like that?"

"Yes, Sir."

"Very well. I want you to keep your promise. Come next time you are free. I shall be expecting you."

He picks up the horse's bridle. I bow – and find he's galloped off before I get a chance to say thank you.

Chapter 3

I can hardly wait until my next free day. I act normally – try to anyway – but sometimes the excitement is difficult to hide. I catch myself singing when I polish the silver, but thankfully the sisters don't hear! The day finally comes when I have some time off and can visit the duke.

I walk backwards and forwards outside the side door of his house for ages, at least five minutes, gathering up the courage to knock. The door is shiny and black with a fierce lion's head for a door knocker. There is a sign by the door, which I can't make any sense of no matter how long I look at the letters.

"But that's why I'm here," I say to myself. I pick up the heavy brass ring in the lion's mouth and knock it against the door three times. The sound echoes inside the house as I wait. My knees are trembling a little. I tell myself it's excitement and not fear!

Footsteps approach from the other side of the door. Before I can decide whether to run away or not, it opens. An elderly man with grey whiskers looks down at me. He is wearing a black jacket, a scarlet waistcoat and white breeches. He looks very smart.

"Yes?" he says. "How can I help you?"

"Please, Sir, my name is Ignatius Sancho," I manage to say before he holds up his hand to stop me.

"You may call me Brydges. I am the duke's butler and he has been expecting you. You are to follow me."

"Yes, Sir," I say, stepping inside a short corridor that opens into a large kitchen. Quite a few people are busy in there. They look up as we come in.

"Sit down. Cook will fetch you a glass of milk while I let the duke know you've arrived."

"Thank you, Brydges," I say, keeping my eyes down as I feel myself being looked at.

When I've drunk the milk, Brydges returns and takes me up some wooden stairs into a grand hall. An enormous display of flowers on a round table fills the air with sweet scents. The flowers are blocking the view of another staircase. It makes me gasp when I first see it. I have never seen stairs like them. They are wider at the bottom and swirl up to the next floor. I need to take two steps on each of the smooth stone treads, and the banister rail is so polished and shiny that I can't help imagining what a thrill it would be to slide down.

At the top of the stairs a footman opens some double doors for us. They lead into the drawing room, where the duke is standing by the fireside waiting for me.

"Ignatius Sancho, Sir," Brydges says, before bowing and going out.

"Welcome, Ignatius," the duke says. "I asked Brydges to bring you up here so that you can meet my wife, the duchess. Sometimes I will be busy when you call and the duchess will look after you."

I bow to the duke and I bow to the duchess. For some reason, my mouth has gone dry and I can't seem to find any words.

"Now let's go back downstairs to the library," the duke says, and I follow him out. We go down those magnificent stairs and I think that, if nothing else, this visit will have been worth it just to walk up and down the staircase.

The duke takes me into a room just off the hall. It is dark compared to the drawing room. All around the room are rows of books, locked away inside wooden cabinets with glass doors. Paintings of ladies and gentlemen hang on some of the walls. One painting shows a man on horseback, who seems to be staring right at me.

"My papa," says the duke, following my gaze.

"Yes, Sir," I say, bowing to the painting. The duke smiles.

"I thought we could have a look at the globe before we do anything else," he says, leading me over to a large, round ball set inside a small table. The ball turns slowly as his hand guides it. So far all I have been able to say is "Yes, Sir" but now my curiosity defeats my shyness.

"What's a globe?" I ask, running over to him. "Please, Sir," I add, remembering my manners.

"It represents our planet, Earth, with all the continents, islands, seas and oceans. It names them all. You can touch it too, if you like."

I put my hand out carefully and feel its smooth surface. It swivels this way and that way as my fingers turn it.

The duke lets me enjoy it for a while and then he points out the British Isles. He traces his fingers over a large expanse of blue and tells me it's called the Atlantic Ocean. Then he comes to some islands far away from Britain.

"Here are the West Indian islands, and here – " he points his finger further down – "here is South America. Do you know where you were born, Ignatius?"

"The sisters say I was born in Africa, Sir, or rather on a ship that was sailing from Africa to South America."

"See if you can find the British Isles again." He waits while

I turn the globe. "That's right! And now turn the globe away from you." The globe spins. "That's it! Stop there."

My fingers are touching a very large area of land indeed.

"That, Ignatius, is Africa."

By the time I lie down in bed that night, my own head is spinning with all the things I have learned. I try and stay awake so I can remember everything, but soon I'm yawning. Could it be that I have found a friend? One who is going to help me reach my goal of learning to read and write? I snuggle down under the blankets, and soon I'm fast asleep.

Chapter 4

After that first visit, I go to Montagu House as often as I can. Sometimes I sit with the duchess, sometimes with the duke and sometimes the whole family gathers around and plays cards while I watch.

Mostly, it's the duchess and I sitting beside each other, looking at books. She reads to me and then she helps me read to her. It is a most wonderful feeling as the letters begin to flow into sounds and words I can say out loud. Also, I like sitting next to her, she smells nice!

When she gets tired of being my schoolteacher she gives me lessons in "etiquette" so that I know how to be polite in company. We practise everything, right from me being introduced, to how I sip tea and make conversation. Brydges joins in. He pulls my shoulders back, tilts my chin up and tells me never to sag! Then he opens the double doors and announces my name. At first, hearing him boom "Ignatius Sancho" makes me want to turn and run – jump on the banisters, zoom to the bottom and sprint through the front door. I almost do it too, once or twice. But after a few times I liked hearing my name. Instead of creeping in through the door like a mouse I hold my head up and smile as I enter the room.

This afternoon we are practising conversation. Brydges introduces me and the duchess stands up as I enter. I bow. Thank goodness I remember that the gentleman never sits down before the lady does.

"Good afternoon, Sancho."

"Good afternoon, Your Grace."

She sits and waves me to sit on the chair beside her. Goodness! Her back is so straight, I'm not sure I can manage but I try. Brydges has, meanwhile, brought the tea things in on a tray which he places on a table beside the duchess. She pours two cups.

"Milk?" she asks. I nod but she shakes her head at me.

"Yes please," I say. She pours a small amount into the teacup.

"Sugar?"

"Yes please," I remember to say this time.

It's a strange feeling. I know how to serve tea, I've been

doing it all my life, but I've never once thought I might one day be drinking tea with a duchess.

Brydges brings my cup and saucer over. I see the duchess holding hers on her lap so I do the same. She is wearing a beautiful apricot-coloured silk dress and I worry the tea might spill on it.

The duchess raises the cup to her lips and takes a very small sip before placing it back on its saucer. "Tell me about yourself, Master Sancho." I am so gripped by the teacup's journey that I don't really hear what she says. Nothing happens and I realize she is looking at me.

"What?" I say.

She smiles. "Better to say 'I beg your pardon, Your Grace' rather than 'What.'"

"Oh yes." I clear my throat. "I beg your pardon, Your Grace?"

This play-acting makes me laugh and my teacup starts to wobble. Brydges steps forward but I manage to take control before it spills. We exchange a look and he winks at me.

"I was asking you to tell me about yourself, Sancho."

I am not sure where to start. But the duchess waits patiently and I soon begin to talk freely. All I can remember is the house in Greenwich, so I have to rely on what I've been told about my life before that: I tell her that I was born on a ship sailing from Africa to the New World, and that my mother died when I was a baby and my father soon after. When I was still very little, I was taken on board another ship, sailing back across the Atlantic Ocean – the very same ocean the duke had showed me on the globe a few months ago – only this time I was heading for England. The sisters say that once I reached London, I was given to them as a present. I don't know if any money changed hands. I think it usually did.

"And here I am, Your Grace, and grateful that the duke noticed me in the park that day."

"The duke is a wonderful man," she says. "He believes that if he can help only one person, it is worth doing."

This is marvellous. I have managed a little conversation and changed the subject! I deserve some tea and drink the whole cup off in one go.

"Would you care for some more tea, Sancho?" The duchess asks.

I look at her. I look at Brydges. He gives me a very small nod.

"Yes please, Your Grace," I say.

Brydges takes my cup over to the little table beside the duchess and she pours us both another cup, exactly like the first. She stirs hers daintily and Brydges brings my cup back.

I stir the sugar in too, being careful not to stir too fast. This tea drinking needs a lot of concentration.

It is now the duchess's turn so I wait. She tells me about a Jamaican man, Francis Williams, who the duke sent to grammar school here in England and then on to Cambridge University.

"When Francis Williams went back to Jamaica both he and the duke hoped the Governor would employ him but, sadly, the Governor refused."

I don't need to ask why. It's because, although Francis Williams was a free man, he was from the African continent, like me. As a small child I didn't know anything but, now I am older I know a bit about the system of slavery, where one person "owns" another and can do whatever they want with that person.

It works like this. Men, women and children are kidnapped from Africa, and stuffed into ships with no room to breathe. The boats travel across the Atlantic Ocean to the West Indies, on a journey known as the Middle Passage. Lots of people get sick and some even die because of the terrible conditions. Their bodies are dropped overboard. Those people still alive are sold and enslaved. They have to work on the plantations there, for no money, and are treated very badly. Many die, but they are replaced by more kidnapped Africans.

The sugar, rum, tobacco and cotton made on the plantations is shipped back to Britain and sold. The ships' owners and the plantation owners make a lot of money, but the enslaved people don't make anything. They *lose* everything: their family, their freedom and, often, their life.

I am enslaved, too, and the whole system makes me feel very cross. I don't think it's right that one person can "own" another person.

"What happened to Francis Williams?" I ask the duchess.

"He opened a school."

"So he can still enjoy his books and help others enjoy them too?"

The duchess nods. I'm glad.

"Thank you, Brydges. You may clear the tea things away. Well done, Sancho, you did very well."

"Can we stop now and go back to being normal?" I say.

"Yes, Sancho, we can. But I need to go upstairs now and change for dinner. Be sure to come back soon."

I love my visits to Montagu House. It's a different world to the house in Greenwich where the sisters are not interested in me. They only think of me as their servant. The duke and duchess always make me feel welcome and, as the months turn into a year, and then two, my skills improve and the sisters' power over me becomes weaker.

Soon, I can read all the shop signs when I go to market and I can even read the sign above the side door at Montagu House. It says:

NOTICE

SERVANTS, DOMESTICS

AND LOWER ORDERS

MUST USE THE

TRADESMAN'S ENTRANCE

Chapter 5

My heart starts thumping as soon I turn over the little piece of card that has dropped on to the front doormat. It's from the duke. I know because I can read now. It says he will visit the sisters at eleven o'clock next Thursday morning.

He keeps telling me he is going to visit and I keep trying to put him off.

"We can't keep your visits a secret any longer, Ignatius, can we? It's not right."

"But—"

"But nothing. Don't worry, I'm sure they will come round to our way of thinking once I tell them how clever you are."

I know the sisters will never agree to me getting an education and I am afraid they will put a stop to my visits to Montagu House, but the duke is sure he can convince them otherwise.

When the morning of the duke's visit arrives, the sisters

are all aflutter. They have no idea why he should be paying them a visit. I've had to give the parlour an extra clean, making sure there is not a speck of dust to be seen. Oldest Sister stands over me as I wind the clock, making sure it's telling the right time. Cook has made delicate biscuits.

At eleven o'clock sharp, there is a knock at the front door. It is the duke, right on time! He winks at me as I let him in. After I take him into the parlour and announce his name, I sit at the top of the stairs where I know they can't see me. I can only hear bits of their conversation, so I creep down a few steps.

The sisters sound dismayed when the duke tells them how we met on Blackheath Common.

"Your Grace, we can only apologize. We had no idea that the boy was bothering you."

"You mistake me, Madam. He is not a bother. I invited him to my house. He is very clever, as clever as any little boy in England. He only needs help with his learning."

"Your Grace is very modern to think a servant needs an education," says Oldest Sister's voice. "We feel, however, that it would not suit the boy."

"May I ask why not?"

"It is perfectly plain, Your Grace. Any effort will be wasted on him. The boy will never amount to anything other than a servant and even the tiniest bit of knowledge will stop him from doing his job properly."

The duke tries a few more times but the sisters absolutely refuse to allow me to have lessons.

"You cannot be serious, Your Grace! It would be the beginning of the end. No, we will not hear of it."

It's almost as if they are afraid. Do they think I am powerful after all?

I knew they wouldn't allow it, but I couldn't help hoping that the duke could change their minds. I struggle to find the moment when their feelings changed towards me. Perhaps I did something wrong? They complain about me becoming an expensive plaything now. I know I'm growing and am forever hungry. My clothes never seem to fit for long and they like me to look the part of a footman, not too shabby, when I go shopping with them to hold their parcels. I am leaving childhood behind and it is not coming back.

I start to feel sorry for myself. However unfriendly, the sisters are the only people I have known for a long time. They are strict, with rigid ideas about what is right and what is wrong, but I suppose they are the closest thing to family I have. And Greenwich is the only place I am used to. Where would I go if the sisters didn't want me any more? I know there are many people, including children, on the streets of London, with no shelter at night and nowhere to cook their food. I feel sorry for them, especially in the winter. It's dangerous for them, because sometimes they are rounded up and transported to the Americas.

As I sit there on the stairs, I ask myself: *who am I?* A big fat tear trickles down my cheek. I brush it away with my hand. I think the sisters want me to feel grateful to them, but I don't. Every now and then, when they think I have been very naughty, they say they will send me back across the ocean and sell me, so that I have to work for nothing on a sugar plantation.

I am not often naughty, but I did steal some biscuits once. It was only because I was hungry and didn't know it was stealing. All I had eaten that day was some porridge and a bowl of soup. I thought Cook had forgotten the tray with the biscuits on it and gone home. I was tidying up for her and wasn't sure what to do with them since they had been out for a few hours and might turn the other biscuits bad if I put them back in the tin. Besides, I reasoned, those biscuits were supposed to have been eaten already. I looked at them sitting on the plate, practically asking me to eat them. So I did.

Later there was a big scene of "Hunt the Biscuits" with the sisters opening cupboards and looking under the table and in the oven. I confessed they were in my tummy.

"We have a thief among us!" Middle Sister said. I was

sent to my room having been struck across my hands with the poker three times, once for each biscuit. They pride themselves on being fair.

The parlour door opens and I snap out of my daydream.

A very sweet voice says, "I suppose pictures cannot hurt." It's Oldest Sister! It doesn't sound like her at all!

"Excellent. Maps – er – picture books – are a marvellous invention," I hear the velvety voice of the duke reply. "Ignatius will enjoy looking at them, I'm sure."

"You do us a great honour, Your Grace, by your visit. The boy will show you out. Sancho!"

That shouting of my name suddenly sounds like the Oldest Sister I know so well.

"The pleasure has been entirely mine," the duke says as he takes his leave of the sisters, shutting them firmly inside the parlour.

At the front door he looks at me seriously. He speaks quietly so the sisters cannot hear. "Well, there it is. I did my best. We won't mention it again. See you next week as usual for your glass of milk?"

I bow and my eyes, still teary, say a thank you. He might not have convinced the sisters to let me learn to read and write, but I am still allowed to go to the duke's house. What I do there is none of their business.

Chapter 6

I continue visiting Montagu House. The days get colder and my glasses of milk become hot chocolate, which I love. Since the duke's visit, we have been spending more time together. At first, I believe everything he says, but soon catch on to his jokes.

"Do you know," he says to me one day, while we are having a snack in his library, "that there are people in this world with two mouths? One for eating, as we are now, and the other, located somewhere at the top of their head, for speaking. It means one can eat and talk at the same time."

"I have even heard of someone," I say, playing along, "who gets so muddled up he gobbles his words and talks nonsense from his head."

"I know him!" the duke says.

It's nice laughing with someone.

One evening, the duke asks Brydges and I to tie opposite

chairs to each other under the dining table. He makes sure the whole family breakfasts together the next morning. I wish I could be there to see them all fighting to sit down. He tells me he could hardly speak from laughing. Luckily, the duchess shares his sense of humour.

I have begun reading the newspapers for the duke as his eyesight is fading. On 1 December, 1739, the duke asks me to read out loud about the Stono Rebellion, a large uprising of enslaved people that happened in September in South Carolina, one of the British colonies in North America.

I pause and peep over the top of the newspaper. The duke is staring out of the window but he doesn't say anything. I'm not even sure if he's listening. However kind the duke is, I never tell him what I think unless he asks me. For instance, I am very sorry that the rebellion was defeated, but I won't mention it.

"Thank you, Brydges," the duke says, as the old butler enters and puts a tray of little biscuits on the table. Brydges bows and goes out. I sigh. If only the sisters were as polite to me, I might feel more content living with them.

I know all the servants in Montagu House now I think, even though there are so many. Too many to count. They clean boots and shoes, look after oil lamps and candles, clean the looking glasses and polish the furniture, take messages, lay the table, clear the table, clean the silver, wash the china and the pots and pans, lay the fires and clean the grates. All the things that have to get done in Greenwich between me, the cook and the maid-of-all-work. To be fair, we don't have as many boots and shoes or as much silver and china, but we are still very busy.

In Greenwich, the cook and the maid don't usually stay long. The work is hard, washing dishes all day, preparing food and cleaning up the kitchen. The maids are usually a little older than me. The current maid-of-all-work is called Betsy, and we get on very well. She is fourteen and I am eleven. We make up songs together and play practical jokes all day, chasing each other up and down the stairs. The sisters hate to see us enjoying ourselves.

I nibble on a biscuit and turn back to the newspaper. The next article is about some boring political scandal.

"Please continue, Ignatius," says the duke. I wish I could stay here, and never go back to Greenwich.

The weather turns very cold on Christmas Eve and every day is frosty. Icicles hang from the roofs. Betsy and I hope that Old Father Thames will freeze over so there can be a frost fair. There hasn't been one for a very long time. Every day we try to get news of what's happening at London Bridge, where the ice forms.

On New Year's Day, we walk to the river and get talking to one of the boatmen. He sends us away saying the ice isn't thick enough yet, but if the weather stays cold, we should come back in a few days as there is bound to be a fair.

We go home very excited. Sure enough, a few days later, the ice thickens and a fair is announced. Hurrah! We decide to ask the sisters if we can go on our day off. I am worried they will say no, but they seem to be in a good mood.

"You may go, but only if you promise to be home by six o'clock," says Oldest Sister.

"We will, Madam," Betsy says.

"And you promise to behave yourselves."

"We do," I say.

"Well, here is the Bible, for you to make your promise on," says Middle Sister, holding up the book.

Betsy and I put our hands on the Bible and make our promise. Then we race out the room before they change their minds!

Before we head to the fair, we visit Betsy's grandmother's house. She gives us some old skates that belonged to Betsy's grandfather when he was a boy. They are a dirty yellow colour and someone has bored holes at either end, Betsy's grandfather perhaps. Leather straps go through these holes, to tie on to your boots. The old lady gives them a tug to make sure the leather is still strong.

"What are the skates made of, Madam?" I ask.

"I believe they're bones," she says.

"Ugh!" says Betsy. "I don't want to wear bones!"

"They're very old," her grandmother says. "Probably from a horse. Go on, give it a try."

It's too exciting not to, so we thank her very much and sling them around our shoulders.

"Remember to look up and not at the ground when you're skating. We don't want you coming home with broken bones!"

"Very funny," I say, as Betsy shuts the front door.

We make our way towards the river. By the looks of it, lots of people have had the same idea. The crowd is in a good mood and someone starts a song in a deep bass voice. Everyone joins in and the sound breaks over us. Smiling faces are everywhere, noses nipped red with cold, steamy breath all around. I glance at Betsy and she looks back at me. Our eyes are dancing. I put my arm around her and give her shoulder a rub.

"Brrr!" she says.

The crowd slows down. We are near London Bridge now and I point it out to Betsy.

"I hope the ice is thick and we don't fall in," she says, screwing up her face.

"Don't you worry about that, luvvie, they got horses and carts out there," says a lady who has been walking beside us for the last half hour. "Worry about your pockets, if anything."

Betsy clutches her sides and breathes a sigh of relief. Her pockets are still there, safely tied underneath her skirts.

"Here we are!" I say. "But where's the river?"

Chapter 7

A street of tents, with people selling all kinds of things, stretches out in front of us. It's hard to believe the water is still there, flowing underneath it all. There are stalls, fire-spits for roasting meat, boats made into sledges and hundreds of people all ready to have fun.

Nearby, a heavy printing press is churning out calling cards and souvenirs. I buy one for Betsy with some coins from my Christmas box. A poem is already printed on it, along with today's date. All it needs is for the letters of her name to be set before being printed off. That doesn't take long and she is thrilled.

"Read the poem, please," Betsy begs. "You know I can't do it."

"Very well," I say, pleased to show off my talent. I clear my throat. Betsy laughs. The words are quite difficult, but I am happy to have a try.

"Behold the liquid Thames now frozen over
That lately ships of mighty burden bore
Here watermen for want to row in boats
Make use of booze to get them pence and groats."

There is general laughter and, to my amazement, a crowd has formed around us, some nudging each other with their elbows. I feel proud that I, an African boy, am able to read when many of these grown men and women can't. But I know it's only because they are poor and haven't had the opportunity. I carry on, hoping to inspire them.

"Here you may print your name, though you cannot write
'Cause numbed with cold: 'tis done with great delight!
And lay it by, that ages yet to come
May see what things upon the ice are done."

Everyone starts clapping and some even give me a few coins! It's a new feeling – to be respected. It makes me feel warm inside and also a little shy. I take a bow, grab Betsy by the elbow and move on past the next stall where they are selling pots and pans.

We find a large area of ice that has been flattened and smoothed to try out our skates. It's surrounded by bundles of hay. Betsy sits down on one and I help her put one of her skates on.

"Is that tight enough?" I ask, pulling the leather straps as tight as I can.

She nods. Once mine are on too we stand up very gingerly and take a few tottering steps. *Whoops!* I lose my balance, only righting it when Betsy holds on to my arms. We clutch each other helplessly.

"You've got to slide," a small boy says as he glides by, making it look easy.

Betsy and I hold hands and set off, moving very slowly but somehow staying upright. We manage to get in step with each other and begin to get the hang of it, sliding first one way and then the other. It's a wonderful feeling! As if I can go anywhere and do anything!

"Isn't that the boatman from the other day?" Betsy says, pointing.

"Hello!" I shout out to him.

He waves. We skate over, but can't stop and end up barging into him!

"Whoa!" He gives a good-natured laugh. "Would you like to go for a sled ride on the river?"

Soon we are sailing along in his boat with some other passengers. Wooden runners have been nailed on underneath the boat and we are pulled along by a horse. It's hard to hear anything as the wind carries our voices away. We go up river, as near as we can to the new bridge being built at Westminster. The boatman reins in his horse so we can look at the constructions.

"They're draining the water out of those piers and putting stones in," the boatman says.

Other piers stretch out in a line across the river with wooden pulleys and water wheels alongside some of them.

"There's so many!" I say.

"There are fourteen piers. They're going to hold up the arches, when they've been built," a passenger puts in.

A thin man with a hat pulled down over his ears and a blue scarf right up to his chin says, "It'll be good to have another bridge, it took me ages to get across London Bridge last week, at least an hour just to get to the other side." He rubs his hands together to keep them warm. "I heard the bells strike eleven in Southwark and twelve noon as I reached the City."

"All I know is, there won't be much need for us any more," the boatman says. "Our trade will drop off sharpish."

"Maybe you'll get some compensation," the first passenger chips in.

The boatman cheers up at this thought. He flaps the reins, turns his horse around and heads back to the fair.

"It's been dark for ages now," Betsy says suddenly.

"I wonder what the time is?" I shoot her a worried glance.

The boat trip has taken longer than we expected. We try not to panic and manage to persuade the boatman to take us some of the way east towards Greenwich, once he has dropped off the other passengers.

"Right, this is as far as I go," he says a short time later. "The ice is getting thinner. Can you hear the different sound it's making?"

It does sound slushier. He steers the horse over to a stone jetty. As he helps us out, I try to pass him the coins given to me earlier.

"Nah, you keep 'em, though I thank ye kindly. Gee up, Ned, let's get back to where I'll charge the next gentleman double, if I think he can afford it."

He turns the boat and gives a laugh as it grates against the stone steps. He raises his hat in farewell and heads off back to the fair. We turn away too and race towards Greenwich.

When we get back, I can tell it's much later than we promised. The house is dark, with only a tallow candle burning on the kitchen table.

"We'll have to say sorry in the morning," I say. "I'm sure they'll understand when we explain."

Betsy yawns. "I hope so," she says. "Ignatius, today was the best day of my life so far."

"Mine too," I agree.

I leave her with the candle as she beds down in the kitchen. I stumble to my room in the attic, trying to be as quiet as possible so as not to wake the sisters.

Chapter 8

In the morning I don't get a chance to see Betsy as Cook has her busy in the kitchen while I am busy in the rest of the house. I go about my work cheerfully. Yesterday was such fun. I'm still glowing from reading the poem to a real live audience, and learning to skate gave me the most wonderful feeling. I am grateful to the sisters for allowing us out and remind myself to say sorry about being late home as soon as I have the chance. I try extra hard with my chores, giving the bedposts an extra polish.

Middle Sister comes upstairs. I smile at her.

"Leave that!" she says. "You are to come downstairs at once, into the parlour." Her voice sounds cold and hard. It gives me a shock.

"Yes, Madam," I say, tucking the duster into my apron. I pick up the broom and dustpan and take them into the kitchen, hoping to see Betsy but she isn't there. I hang up my apron and put the broom and dustpan away before knocking on the parlour door.

Betsy is standing in front of the sisters. All three of them are sitting straight-backed in their chairs, looking very stern. Betsy catches my eye and shakes her head – a signal the sisters are not in a good mood.

"Thank you for joining us, Master Sancho. We don't mind waiting, do we, sisters?" Youngest Sister mocks.

"Sorry," I mumble. This hasn't started well.

"You broke your promise and betrayed out trust," Oldest Sister begins. "We trusted you to return by six o'clock and you did not. You took advantage of our good nature. What have you to say?"

Although I'm nervous, I hold my head up. Spending time with the duke and duchess has made me more confident.

"We're very sorry, we didn't mean to," I say in a firm voice. "We went for a boat ride and it took much longer than we thought. We saw the new bridge that is being—"

"That is of no interest to us," Oldest Sister interrupts.

"It gets dark so early that it was hard to guess the time," Betsy says, backing me up.

"That is a poor excuse and I am inclined to think it a lie."
Oldest Sister's voice is even colder than usual.

Betsy's eyes flash. "It's what happened," she says. "Don't call me a liar."

The three sisters look at one another. I apologize again, worried Betsy has gone too far. I try to tell them it was my fault, that I should have checked the time or asked the boatman how long the trip would take before we set off.

Oldest Sister cuts me off again. "If anything, Betsy is the older one, she should take the blame."

I try to protest, but Oldest Sister holds her hand up to silence me.

"Betsy?"

She does not reply. The clock in the parlour ticks loudly in the silence. While I'm racking my brains for something to say that might make everything better, Oldest Sister starts talking again.

"You betrayed our trust. And, talking of trust, we have noticed that you both behave badly."

"I beg your pardon?" says Betsy.

"You are too friendly. We do not think it healthy."

"Not healthy to be friends?" Betsy exclaims.

"Not healthy, I say. First, you are friends and then who knows where that will lead? Betsy, we hold you responsible for leading Sancho astray. You are a bad influence. You are discharged. You will leave this house immediately. We will not have your sort working for us."

I am not sure what they are talking about, but Betsy is furious.

"Sacked for being friends? Ignatius and I are friends, yes. I am happy to count him as one. He behaves as well as the next person, if not better. How dare you accuse otherwise."

"I will dare what I like in my own house, Madam. How dare *you* answer back!"

"You think bad things because you are mean inside," Betsy shouts, no longer caring what she says. I admire her courage and for sticking up for me. No one has ever done that before.

"I don't want to work for you any more anyway. I hate you," she says. When she reaches the door, she turns and looks at me. "Don't listen to them, Ignatius – this isn't really why they're sacking me. They just hate to see people happy because they're so miserable. Good luck, you're going to need it!" She leaves the room and bangs the door shut.

For what seems like ages the only sound is the ticking of the clock.

"As for you, Master Sancho, we are stuck with you, for the moment," Oldest Sister says finally. "We will not sack you –

you have nowhere to go – but we will think very hard about sending you to the West Indies if you do not improve. Any more betrayals or broken promises, mark my words, we shall send you to Barbados."

Betsy's outburst has made me brave and I imagine her listening behind the door.

"I'll write you a letter," I say with a half-smile.

Oldest Sister's face settles into that familiar expression of stone – not just stone, brimstone – straight from Hell. Then she smiles thinly. It makes me shudder. A smile should spread warmth but hers gives off ice.

"Don't think we won't," she says. "You may leave the room."

There is no Betsy behind the door. My heart is empty and I'm finding it hard to breathe. I'm used to sharing my life with Betsy and now suddenly she is gone.

I wish I could disappear, like Betsy, but it's true I have nowhere to go. No grandmother's arms to hug me and no one in the world to love me. I run upstairs into my room at the top of the house, where I throw my arms around the pillow and bite into it. Sometimes I want to laugh and sometimes I want to cry, but if I cry I might never stop.

*

The sisters do not let me out of the house for a month, except to run their errands, which I must complete as fast as I can or face a beating. I lay awake long into the night thinking about Betsy, and about the Duke and Duchess of Montagu who I have not seen for many weeks. Do they miss me? I miss them from the bottom of my heart. I feel friendless and alone, trapped like the fish beneath the ice of the frozen Thames.

The first thing I do when I can go out is visit Betsy's grandmother. I hope Betsy will be staying there, while she looks for a new job. Betsy's grandmother opens the door as soon as I knock, but she is already shaking her head before I've finished my question.

"Sorry, love," Betsy's grandmother says. "Betsy's gone to Northamptonshire to work in a big house belonging to Lord and Lady Somebody-or-other. She won't be coming back for at least a year, maybe longer."

I walk slowly back to the house. I decide the best thing I can do for myself, and for Betsy, is concentrate on the things that make me feel happy. That way I won't let the sisters get to say who I am. After all, being their servant does not mean I am a lesser person than them. I think about sending Betsy a letter, to tell her my plan, but then I remember she can't read, so it won't be any use.

Betsy showed me what it's like to have a friend and our day at the frost fair showed me what it's like to feel free. I will find those things again. I still have my friendship with the duke and duchess and, if I cannot escape the sisters, I will gain my freedom through books, music and dancing. These things will cheer me up and transport me to places I cannot actually go. I am not putting my head in the sand – this is serious, it is about survival. My own.

Chapter 9

1749

Ten years have passed since Betsy left the house. Even though I haven't seen her again, I still think of her every now and then. She was the first person my own age I could call a friend. Sadly, her grandmother died shortly after she left, so there is no way I can find Betsy now.

I have tried to keep my vow of staying cheerful and mostly I have succeeded, though there are times when I feel like giving up. I do get fed up serving the sisters – breakfast, lunch, tea and supper, and clearing up after them with not a single word of thanks. Ever. In fact, they seem to have gone from disliking me to being afraid of me. They leave the room whenever I enter. I can't help it if I'm bigger than them now, and my voice is deeper. They still call me "Boy" even though I am almost twenty-one years old.

I also find it hard to feel cheerful when I am made fun of in the street. It's often to do with the colour of my skin.

Groups of workmen and even well-dressed people shout stupid things about me, and laugh among themselves. I ignore their insults as much as I can and notice they are not so loud-mouthed when out walking alone. Cowards! It's sad they have to invent reasons why they think someone with darker skin is not as clever or as good-looking, to make themselves feel better. I wonder why having white skin makes some people feel grander than everyone else? It's a mystery to me.

The duke is not like that and neither was Betsy. Instead of worrying, in summer I pick roses from the garden while they are still wet with dew. I arrange them in vases, just like the ones in Montagu House, only not so splendid. I don't think the sisters even notice them, but they make me feel better whenever I walk past.

I save all my pennies until I can buy myself a theatre ticket. I could watch David Garrick all day and all night! He is just as good at comedy as tragedy. As the new manager of the Drury Lane Theatre, he has had it redecorated and it's a wonderful place to go to on my days off. The whole of London seems to be there and, while I am part of the audience, I can forget that I am only a servant with no chance of becoming anything else.

I watch the sailors at the wharves dance the hornpipe

and learn it myself. I love to dance, either a solemn minuet or a wilder country one. There are servants' dances that I attend from time to time. My favourite dances are the Scottish ones – especially the Threesome Reel. I make up tunes and these get played at our servants' dances sometimes, which pleases me. I dance with the maids-of-all-work that come after Betsy and even twirl the cook when she isn't expecting it.

At the duke's house, I learn about musical composition and poetry. The more I try, the better I get, and the better I get, the more interesting life becomes. I read famous authors, like Jonathan Swift or poets like Alexander Pope. I like Pope better because he makes me laugh as well as think.

But in the summer of 1749, something terrible happens. The duke, after a violent fever that comes on quite suddenly, dies.

The last time I see him is the evening of 1 July. The day has been hot and sticky, but his library is cool. He invites me to sit down in an armchair opposite him.

"Ignatius, you first came here as a boy who couldn't read or write and look at you now, a young man with many talents," he says, his eyes alight. "I don't think I have any more to teach you. I hope you will continue to visit us. Please feel free to use the library whenever you wish."

I smile at him. Sometimes we don't need words.

He stands up and goes over to his desk. "I have a little present for you."

I get up and join him. There is a long parcel in his hand.

"Open it," he says. Inside is a set of new quills. I have been using slate pencils to write with and old quills that have seen better days. These new ones look sharp and sleek. They are made from a variety of bird's feathers. "I hope you like them."

I want to cry with happiness.

"Sir, without your help I would still be writing with my finger in the cold ashes of a fireplace, still struggling with my letters, still ill-informed about the world," I say. "I am so grateful. Thank you."

"Nonsense! It's you who has put in the hard work. Yes, I admit, the duchess and I helped, but only with the mechanics. You are now using your skill to write your own verses and compose music, something I have never even tried! I am very proud of you, Ignatius."

In that moment, my heart swells. I leave the duke's house with a spring in my step. But a week later, he is gone. Brydges comes round to tell me the news, his face pale and sombre. I am so shocked I hardly hear him. The duke was the kindest person I knew, and not just to me. He loved life and believed in a fair society. For instance, I know he gave lots of money to the Foundling Hospital, a home for abandoned children. He really felt that all people needed was a chance to make their own life better, and he was prepared to give them that chance.

Even if I am the only one to ever read my own poems or play my tunes, I know my life is richer for having written them. That makes me happy and I know it made the duke happy too. I will miss him always.

Chapter 10

Late one Sunday afternoon, a few weeks after the duke's death, I am clearing the tea things away when Oldest Sister says, "Sancho, you need to pack a travelling bag for tomorrow. We are going on a trip."

"Yes, Madam. Shall I prepare one for each of you too?"

"No." There is an awkward pause. "Thank you. We shall prepare our own bags."

Immediately, I am suspicious. Firstly, because none of them have ever thanked me for anything, ever, and secondly, because they never do anything for themselves if I can do it for them.

"Where shall we be going?" I ask.

Again, there is an awkward pause.

"It is to be a surprise."

I bow slightly before carrying out the tray and putting it in the kitchen. My heart is beating fast.

As I pass by the bottom of the stairs on my way to light the fires in the bedrooms, I hear Oldest Sister talking quietly in the parlour.

"The cart will call for him at eight o'clock so we must make sure everything seems normal first thing in the morning. Mr Letts has already given me a note payable, which I will take to the bank as soon as Sancho is on board."

On board? A sweat breaks out on my forehead. I have to hold on to the banister as I make my way upstairs. I know what this means. The sisters are going to sell me. They're really going to do it, instead of just threatening me with it. Tomorrow morning, they plan to put me on a ship sailing to the West Indies!

Inside my bedroom at the top of the house, I hear the deep chimes of midnight from the parlour clock. My eyes droop but I jerk awake and decide to stand up. My bag is prepared, but not for the reason the sisters think.

I need to stay awake. One o'clock passes, two o'clock. I have already decided that if I sneak away too early, the Watch might arrest me. They police the streets at night and I would be taken to jail, or to the Bow Street Runners or, heaven forbid, brought back to the sisters. Or I might meet a press gang and find myself bundled in a sack and taken on board a ship to sail the seven seas anyway, until I am old and no longer strong. I need to take my future into my own hands. There is no other choice.

Would it be better to get up at the normal time, make all the normal noises and then slip out of the door? No, I wouldn't get very far if one of the sisters shouted for me early, as they do sometimes. Better to stick with my original plan. I rub my eyes.

Four o'clock chimes downstairs. I must have dozed. I pick up my travelling bag and, at the last minute, pull the blanket off my bed and fold it around my arm. I open the latch and listen carefully before stepping out on to the landing. I stop to allow my eyes to adjust to the new darkness. All I can hear is my heart thumping as I creep down the wooden stairs on to the landing below where the sisters' bedrooms are. Again, I stop to listen and hear regular breathing from behind the doors. I continue creeping down the last set of stairs, missing out the third step from the bottom as that one creaks a lot. Now, along the corridor and into the kitchen.

The last thing I want is to accidentally knock something and make a crash. I hold my bag low and skirt around the kitchen table, put it down before turning the key of the back door. I oiled it with a little left-over butter before I went to bed, so it doesn't make a sound. I open the door but there is a big creak after all. I forgot to oil the hinges! An impulse makes me want to shut the door and scamper back into the comfort of my bed. But it's not safe there any more. By tomorrow my bed will be a thing of the past and I shall be on a sea voyage into certain slavery.

There is no safety on the other side of the door either but I have to keep moving forward. I pull the door open quickly, grab my bag and remember to shut the door slowly to create as little draught as possible. I don't want the cold air to travel up the staircase and wake anyone.

My fingers are trembling so much and my chest is heaving. There is no turning back now. I walk carefully around the house to the front and climb over the low wall on to the street without touching the gate, I know that creaks a lot and Oldest Sister sleeps at the front of the house. I need to get away fast now, and put as much distance as I can between me and the sisters before my escape is discovered.

I know where I'm going.

As well as the darkness, there is a fog coming off the river. My teeth are chattering from fright and the cold that has reached right down into my bones. I unfold the blanket tucked under my arm and throw it over my head and shoulders. Hopefully, if the Watch see me, they will think I am a woman out early to start her work.

Although the quickest way is across Blackheath Common, I'm too afraid of who, or what, I might meet, so I stick to the roads. By the time I am near my destination there are a few people setting out to work. I mingle with them until I reach Montagu House. I will wait in the shadows across the road until a tradesman knocks at the side door or until I see someone moving about in the kitchen. I can't afford to knock too early and cause a commotion.

Chapter 11

Brydges ushers me into the drawing room. I know it so well, even in the half-dark; the chintz sofas, the velvet curtains. He goes over to the long windows at the front of the house and opens the curtains a fraction, letting in a shaft of morning light.

He looks at me and sighs. "I shall fetch Her Grace now. Good luck."

I told Brydges my plan when he let me in; about asking the duchess if I might stay at Montagu House. Until he says those words, I haven't thought that she might refuse. What have I done? What if she says no? Then I will have nowhere to go. I will not only be homeless but also a runaway, always on the lookout in case I am captured.

I shudder and straighten up. There is no choice, I remind myself. If I had stayed in Greenwich any longer, I would be on my way to the ship at this very moment. Anything will be better than that.

Brydges opens the door and the duchess comes in, still in her dressing gown and nightcap. He remains standing by the door. She sits on the sofa where we have had so many happy times before.

"Ignatius! This is an unexpected call and so early in the morning. Has something happened?"

"Your Grace," I stammer. I haven't prepared anything and I don't know what to say. "Your Grace," I start again. She sees my distress.

"Ignatius, sit down. Take your time. Tell me what is going on."

Instead of sitting I drop to my knees in front of her.

"All I ever want to do is read books. And make music. Your house is the only happy place I know. Being here comforts me like nothing else can."

"I'm glad to hear that, Ignatius, but you didn't need to come so early to tell me."

"Take me into your service, Your Grace, please," I eventually blurt out. "I have left the house in Greenwich."

"Goodness," she says.

After a long pause when I dare not look at her, she leans forward and puts her hand on my shoulder. "You know I can't do that, Ignatius. It is very bad form to steal another's servant. What would they do without you?"

"They don't want me! They are selling me, sending me away, back into slavery."

"Surely not? They are just cross with you. It will pass, like it has before."

"I had to pack my bag last night. They mean it this time. The ship sails this morning."

The duchess stands up and walks over to the window. The sunlight catches her face and I see she has got older, and sadder, since the duke died. She doesn't speak for a long time.

"I wish I could help," she says finally. "I know the duke, God rest his soul, would want me to, but how can I? You are asking too much of me, Ignatius. I'm sorry but I must refuse. Brydges will give you some food from the kitchen and I will give you a purse with some coins. But that is all. You must go back to the sisters or make your own way in the world."

A cry escapes me. "I can't go back there! All I know are those four walls but, even so, I can't go back."

The duchess looks at me. I need her to understand.

"They look at me sideways and lock every single cupboard in the house. When they go to bed at night, they lock their bedroom doors. Why? I am not a thief! I am not a murderer! I'm still the same boy they've known since I was two years old. They brought me up. I don't know why life changed – from them dressing me up as their plaything to being scared of me – but their fear has nothing to do with me and all to do with their opinion of who they think I am."

I'm breathing hard. A moment ago I couldn't speak, but now I cannot stop.

"I believe it is a change in them and not in me. However hard life is, I know it is better than what they're planning." I shudder. "If you can't help me then I'll take my chances on the streets."

The duchess is silent.

"You have always shown me a welcome," I continue. "Forgive me if I have asked too much. I didn't know who else to turn to. I know you must be feeling very sad at the moment, missing the duke. I miss him too. I thought, perhaps, I might be able to help cheer you up."

The duchess has tears in her eyes.

Just then, Brydges clears his throat. "Your Grace, if I may?" he says.

She waves a hand for him to continue.

"Your Grace, you know I am about to retire. I have been in your service since you were a girl, coming with you to Montagu House from your parents. You will need a new butler very soon. Ignatius seems well equipped for the job. He has good manners and is cheerful. He learns quickly, we already know that. I will teach him what to do. I will show him myself, and you will have a new butler exactly how you like, without having to search."

The duchess looks at Brydges. Then she looks at me.

Brydges gives it one last try. "He is so helpful already. All the other servants know him and like him, Your Grace. It will be a seamless transition."

I hold my breath.

"Very well," she says. "I will clear it with the sisters, and you shall be my new butler, Ignatius." She manages a small smile. "Welcome to the family."

The duchess visits the sisters later that morning. I am not quite sure what happens but I suspect she gives them the same money they were to receive from Mr Letts, maybe even a little more. I do not like the idea that the duchess has "bought" me, but I know it is the only way she could ever get the sisters to agree to our plan.

I do not return to the house in Greenwich. I do not see the sisters ever again. I believe I did them a favour running away. They had grown afraid of me and I'm sure were not sorry to see me go, although they must have been furious when they woke up and discovered me gone. I think of writing them a letter but in the end decide not to. It would not be a kind letter and I have no wish to relive those hard times. There is no need to scold them. I feel sorry for them; there is no joy in their lives.

I get given a livery – a kind of uniform that servants of wealthy people wear, so everyone knows who they work for. Ours is made up of a red and gold waistcoat, a black jacket with gold buttons and all our linen is white. I've never worn such fancy clothes and feel very hoity-toity. It doesn't stop at clothes either. Our carriages and sedan chairs are painted the same colours, with the Montagu emblem emblazoned on the sides. I love being part of the Montagu household, it is completely different to Greenwich. There are parties and dinners and visits to the country. It is all so grand!

The day comes when Brydges is set to retire. I perch at the end of his bed while he packs away his things. He looks at me, as though he's suddenly remembered something, goes to bend down, then changes his mind. He sits beside me instead.

"I'm leaving one or two things for you, Ignatius, seeing as you're going to be taking over my room."

"That's very kind of you, Brydges."

"It's a strange present, but a useful one. I've had it a long time. It lives under the bed."

I think I know what it's going to be. I'm not sure if I want to see.

"You can take a look, don't be shy."

I take a peek and there is his old chamber pot!

"Thank you, Brydges. I'm sure it will be very useful!"

He is a dear old gentleman.

"And don't forget, the duchess likes—"

"—the crusts cut off her bread, yes, you told me."

Brydges looks at me and smiles. "Just so. Well, I do believe I've taught you everything you need to know, Sancho."

"Thank you, Brydges. You've changed my life, you know. I'm going to miss you very much."

It's true, but I am also excited to take over my new duties tomorrow. I will open the front door and announce visitors, be in charge of some of the other servants and look after all the china plates and silver cutlery. I want to do my job well and it is so much better than being shouted at by the sisters.

Chapter 12

1751

I live in Brydges's old room in the attic, which I love. It's an airy space, with a couple of chairs and a desk, as well as the bed. The window looks out over the park where I used to wander as a small boy and visit the gravel pits.

One evening, as the night is drawing in, I light two candles and settle down to read. I can't decide which book – Laurence Sterne's *The Abuses of Conscience* or Henry Fielding's enormously long novel *The History of Tom Jones, a Foundling*. I choose the Fielding for tonight. It makes me laugh out loud and is excellent at describing the times we live in. Henry Fielding is an interesting man. As well as writing novels he is a lawyer. He is the one who set up the Bow Street Runners, the people I was so frightened of when I ran away two years ago.

Before I get very far into the chapter, however, there is a knock at the door.

"Come in," I say, putting a red silk ribbon between the pages, marking where I am, and closing the book.

A young lad enters. He is tanned and strong, with blonde hair and eyebrows. Even though he is almost as tall as I am, my guess is he is only about fourteen or fifteen.

"Excuse me, Sir," he says.

Imagine! Someone calling me Sir!

"It's William, isn't it?" I ask. The lad is a new hire. I had seen him tacking up the horses under the watchful eye of the head groom as I walked across the stable yard this morning. "Are you settling in all right? Is there something I can help you with?"

"Please, Sir, I was told that you are good with the learning and I need to let my ma know that I arrived safely."

"Call me Sancho, William. You want me to write a letter home?"

He beams at me. "Yes, Mr Sancho, Sir. If you can make it pretty, but easy on the eye? No one in my family reads well."

"I shall do my best, William, but letters are supposed to be a little flowery."

William looks disappointed at this news.

"But I'm quite new at this," I continue. "So it will be a little rough and ready just the same. What is it you want to say?"

He brightens. "Only that I arrived safely."

"That will hardly be worth the penny that will be charged for it."

"But that is all I have to say."

"Very well. We shall keep it to one sheet of paper and seal it up without an envelope, for that will double the price."

William looks puzzled. "They count the envelope as another sheet of paper?"

"They do indeed. That's why so many people write cross-hatched these days, to save money."

"What does cross-hatched mean?" William says, his eyes darting towards the door, as if he is sorry for knocking.

"You write across the page as normal and then you turn the page on to its side and write across it again."

He considers this for only a second. "Better not. Pa only writes his name and Ma will get very confused."

"The brain does get boggled, I agree. Now, you must think of what to write while I prepare the materials."

This is the first time anyone has asked me to write for them and I feel a little under pressure – I've only ever practised writing letters to myself! I talk through what must be done before I commit pen to paper as a way to remind myself.

"First, I must sharpen the quills,' I say, reaching for one. These are the same ones I received from the old duke when he was alive and, although they have been used a lot since then, some still work quite well.

I reach into the writing slope on my desk and pull out my penknife. Then I pick up a crow's quill. These make quite fine writing but, on second thoughts, I put it back. The swan's quill has a thick nib and the letters will be too big, so I pick up the goose quill. That will be perfect. I trim the end with my penknife until it is pointed.

"Hmmm, the ink has dried out," I say, peering into the inkwell.

William has been moving from one foot to the other. Now his shoulders droop.

"Not to worry, I can fix that," I say.

I add some lampblack from a jar that I keep, along with some alcohol and a little gum arabic. I stir them up to make the liquid sticky. I start hunting in the drawer.

"Now what are you looking for?" asks William, standing behind me, watching my every move.

"We must make sure the paper is not of the shiny sort, otherwise the ink will slide all over the place."

Once I've selected the right paper, I place it on the writing slope.

"I'm sorry I bothered you. It seems a lot of work. I had no idea."

"I'm happy to write on your behalf, William," I say, my quill freshly dipped and poised over the paper. "Now, how shall we begin? 'Most Esteemed Parents'?"

William looks horrified. "They'll wonder what language we speak in London! Keep it plain. 'Dear Ma, I am here safe. Your son, William.' That will be plenty."

"Very well."

I'm careful to keep my hand as upright as possible and make a swift stroke downwards with the quill, but I have waited too long and the ink splodges on the page.

"Oh dear!" William's face crumples.

I quickly continue with the other letters to use up the inky blob. This works quite well and soon I have written the first sentence, much to William's relief – and mine.

"Do you have any brothers or sisters, William?"

"Yes, two sisters, Jenny and Robyn."

"Shall you send them a message?"

He thinks for a moment. "'Please pull Jenny's pigtails for me and tell Robyn I have eaten all her scones already.'"

As I write the letters William leans forward and concentrates with me. When it is complete I sit back with satisfaction. We are about halfway down the page.

"What about your father, William? Shall you send him a message too?"

William's brow furrows and then his face brightens. "Tell Pa I hope he's managing the horses without me." He laughs. "Pa hates mucking out the horses, that was always my job. See how he likes it now."

"We shan't include that last bit."

William leans in again and watches me write down what he has just said. I notice the interest he is taking.

"Would you like to read and write, William?"

"Oh no, I couldn't do it," he says. "I wanted to go to Dame school, but Pa said I was a dunce so there'd be no point."

"That's not right, William. No one should be called a dunce. They either have not had the opportunity to learn, or not been taught in the way that suits them."

William looks at me. "Is that true?"

"It most certainly is. Would you like me to teach you?"

William is taken aback. "Well – if you really think I could – and you have the time – I'd like that very much. Thank you, Sir."

I look at William and raise one eyebrow.

"Thank you, Sancho," he corrects himself, smiling.

"With pleasure, William."

I can never repay the duke and duchess for teaching me. I will be forever grateful to them for sharing their good fortune and the only way I can think of paying them back is by doing the same for someone else.

"Right, we shall finish off now. Yours –" I pause, thinking out loud – "Affekshun – efectshun – no, not 'affectionately' for, to be honest, I am not sure if I can spell it. We'll just put: Your son, William."

William nods.

I put the quill down and sprinkle sand over the ink to help it dry, blowing off the extra grains. I fold the letter and take a stub of red sealing wax from the slope, holding it over the candle flame to soften it. Once the wax begins to melt, I let it drip down on to the fold of the letter and stamp it.

"There. Sealed. Now, William, what is your father's name?"

"The same as mine. William Powell. But send it to my ma."

"To Mrs William Powell," I say as I make the letters. "And where do they live?"

"Under Burrow Farm, Shropshire."

"There. The address is done. Give it to the postman tomorrow and trust your ma will have the penny for it when it arrives."

Soon William is gone and I find that letter writing has quite exhausted me.

Half an hour later my head is on the pillow. I wish I had someone to write to. Someone who wanted to know if I arrived safely or not. But I am happy and proud. I wasn't just practising writing this time – I helped William to stay in touch with his family. My writing had a purpose to it.

PART 2

USING MY VOICE

Chapter 13

About six months after I write that letter, William has done so well in our lessons that I suggest promoting him to footman. The duchess agrees, and he has soon charmed the whole household with his good manners.

One morning he knocks on the door of my little office beside the kitchen. There are sheets of paper all over the desk, bills from the local shopkeepers. I've been trying to add them together, but my mind is on something else. The duchess's personal maid burst into my room earlier that morning, all out of breath. She told me the duchess had collapsed when she got out of bed, and begged me to send for the doctor straight away. It is not the first time I have been asked to call for him this month. I let him into the house about an hour ago, and have not heard from him since.

"What is it, William?"

"I'm to fetch you upstairs, Sancho," he says, looking very serious.

"Whatever's the matter? Is the duchess all right?"

"I don't know. I was told to come and get you."

I'm even more worried now. William takes me up the grand staircase, which I am very used to now, and leads me into the drawing room. Instead of the duchess, the doctor is standing there, looking out of the large windows at the front. He turns when I come into the room, and indicates for William to leave us.

"Sancho, you might want to sit down."

I shake my head and remain standing. The doctor sighs. "I have some bad news," he says gently. "I am very sorry to tell you that the duchess has died. She passed at ten o'clock this morning. I am not sure of the exact cause but, as you know, she has been unwell for a while."

"What?" I say. I hear a ringing in my ears. It feels as if all the air has been sucked from the room. "What did you say?"

He has to repeat himself three or four times before I can believe him.

"The duchess? Gone?" I say. I know I sound like a child, but my heart is breaking. My duchess! The kindest lady in the world. She and the duke changed my life. I can't imagine life without her. "Oh, my poor lady!"

The doctor comes over and puts a firm hand on my shoulder. "I'm relying on you to tell the rest of the household. Then you are to wait for instructions from the family."

I pull myself together. I must remember I am no longer the lost little boy the duke and duchess rescued, but a grown man and a butler. I will grieve later, in private. At the moment I need to stay composed, for the household's sake. "Yes, doctor, of course."

I see the doctor out and then go downstairs to break the sad news to the rest of the servants.

The duchess's daughter, Mary, and her husband, George, will be taking over the title and moving into the house shortly. They will become the new Duke and Duchess of Montagu. We expect they will bring their own servants with them. On top of feeling sad, we are all worried that we will lose our jobs. One by one we are called into the dining room and told what will happen to us. Most of the servants are found other jobs in different households. Some of the older ones are given a small pension. When my turn comes, I don't know what to expect. The new duke and duchess are bringing their own butler with them, so I am to leave the service of the Montagu household. But it turns out the old duchess has left me an annual income! Thirty pounds a year to be exact, payable each and every year. She has also left me a legacy, a lump sum of seventy pounds. This means, for the first time in my life, I am free.

I leave the room crying – with sadness and happiness at the same time. The duchess understood exactly what I needed to make my life my own. Thirty pounds a year will not allow me to live like a king, but it does mean that I can rent a room and have food in my stomach without needing a job to pay for it all.

I find a room in a little street off St James. It's no Montagu House, but it's in a good neighbourhood where it's easy to walk everywhere. It's true that street smells waft through the windows sometimes and that it is not only me eating the cheese! I battle with the mice most nights. They are very stubborn neighbours. Still, I am very pleased with it.

I buy another set of clothes and then start to live the life of a gentleman! I have no duties, nor do I need to open the door for anyone or polish any silver. I write music during the days and visit theatres in the evenings.

One evening, I watch my favourite actor, David Garrick, in one of his performances. He is incredible as Richard III. They say it's a very brave actor who takes that role on these days as, back in 1741 when David Garrick first performed it, he shot to instant success and fame.

After the final curtain, I feel I must congratulate him and join the crowd already gathered at the stage door, waiting for David Garrick to appear. We men are lounging about, trying to look fashionably casual in our new woollen frock coats, while the women are decked out wonderfully in colourful dresses. A cheer goes up as David Garrick appears and everyone claps.

"You've changed theatre for ever," one of the gentlemen says to him with a bow.

"Thank you," David Garrick bows in return.

"You're a legend, Mr Garrick," a lady with an enormous wig tells him.

"Thank you, Madam, and I must say, you look spectacular."

She curtsies and fans herself vigorously, looking around in triumph.

He bows again, and again, thanking each person as they try to outdo each other with their compliments. Eventually, after smiling and thanking everyone, he catches my eye.

"Ignatius Sancho." I bow. "Thank *you*, from the bottom of my heart."

This seems to please him. He comes over and we have a short conversation. Then, he asks me to join him for dinner! I feel thrilled as the crowd parts for Mr Garrick and myself.

At a restaurant around the corner, we order roast goose and wash it down with bottles of red wine. We laugh ourselves silly as he tells me about all the little things that went wrong behind the scenes during tonight's performance. I find myself telling him my life story, up to the present moment.

He looks at me thoughtfully. "So, you need a job?"

"Well, not just yet. But I shall eventually, I think."

"Why not be an actor yourself?" he suggests.

"Me?" I am flattered! I've always thought I might make a good actor, ever since that day with Betsy at the frost fair!

Maybe it's the wine, but Mr Garrick promises to help me with my performance, and I find myself agreeing! I'll try anything once.

We talk about which part I should play. I suggest Othello, a part written for a Black man in a play by Shakespeare. But Mr Garrick thinks I would do better with the play *Oroonoko*, which is about an African prince who is kidnapped and enslaved. I am happy to try that part. Mr Garrick is very well-known for playing Shakespearean roles. Maybe he doesn't want my performance to be compared with his. I might be better than him! We meet the very next day. David – as Mr Garrick asks me to call him – arrives with scripts of *Oroonoko* and we settle down to read the play. It is written by a lady, Aphra Behn, and I am impressed. After reading it through, however, I feel quite alarmed. There are a lot of lines to learn! David is very encouraging.

"Just don't speak so fast," is all he says.

After a few weeks' rehearsal, with David patiently giving me voice lessons, he says I'm ready. Unexpectantly reading in front of a small crowd at the frost fair is a completely different feeling to waiting for the curtain to go up on opening night in a crowded theatre I discover. I can hear the audience chatting on the other side. I feel ready, although my mouth is dry and my tummy is doing somersaults. I give myself a shake. The stage manager nods at me and the curtain goes up on Ignatius Sancho – also known as Oroonoko! Here we go!

David comes to the stage door afterwards. There are no crowds. There is no instant success or fame.

"I remembered all my lines!" I tell him, rather out of breath.

"Yes, you did! Well done!" he says, clapping me on the back. "But you galloped along, as if it was a race rather than a play!"

Apparently, no one understood a word I was saying! In the excitement of it all, I got faster and faster. We go back to our restaurant and have a very merry evening laughing at my disastrous stage debut.

"Well, I think we should admit defeat. It seems I am not cut out to be an actor after all!"

"Never mind, Ignatius, you're still a very fine fellow."

Bless Mr Garrick, he thinks anyone can be an actor and doesn't appreciate his own talent. Still, at least I gave it a go.

Chapter 14

1757

I go along quite happily for a few years. The only thing missing is someone to share my good fortune with. But at a servants' dance, around Christmastime, I find that someone. Or rather, that someone finds me.

I attend the dance with my good friend John Osborne, who I met at one of the anti-slave trade meetings I've started going to. We gather together around the city and discuss how the Trade can be ended. The meetings are serious, for it is a serious subject, but at the dance I am seeing another side of John, as he laughs and jokes and twirls maids across the dance floor.

"Right, Sancho," says John, grabbing my arm. "There's someone I want you to meet."

He guides me across the hall, weaving in and out of the dancing couples, until we reach the other side. He leads me to a West Indian woman in a blue dress with a beautiful smile, tapping her feet along to the music. As the music comes to a close, John clears his throat. The woman looks up at him, then at me.

"May I present Ignatius Sancho. Sancho, this is my sister, Anne."

I like her straight away. She laughs at my jokes and isn't silly herself – a winning combination! We begin walking out together, and it soon becomes clear that we share the same interests and make each other feel happy.

The following autumn, I am sitting up in bed one morning, lazily brushing crumbs off the sheet and thinking about how lucky I am. A nearby church bell rings the hour. *Goodness*, I think. *Is that the time?* I leap out of bed. I am due to take Anne to New Spring Gardens on the south side of the river in an hour's time! I take a long time deciding which coat I should wear. I want to make a good impression today, especially. My fingers have trouble doing up the buckles on my shoes. I need to calm myself down and not rush about doing too many things at once.

"Breathe, Sancho," I say to myself as I put a small box into my waistcoat pocket. I make sure it's safe, then head out on to the streets of London.

Soon Anne and I are strolling across Westminster Bridge

in the late autumn sunshine. We stop to look over the parapet, and watch Old Father Thames lazily stirring. I want to put my arm around her waist but she might not like it, so I don't.

"Did you know this bridge opened in 1750? I saw its foundations being built at a frost fair I went to a long time ago."

"Really?" says Anne, raising her face up to the sun. She looks so beautiful.

"Yes. London is growing westwards, thanks to the bridge's success. I do believe the boatmen got compensation, because fewer and fewer people use the boats to cross the river."

"Indeed." Anne looks at me and smiles.

"Quite a few bridges are being talked of now and there are far fewer boatmen around these days."

Anne smiles at me again. *Goodness! Get à hold of yourself, Sancho*, I think to myself. *What are you blathering on about bridges for?*

"Shall we continue?" I say, patting the little box in my waistcoat pocket, to make sure it's still there.

When we arrive at New Spring Gardens it's already crowded with young couples and groups walking along the wide, neatly trimmed avenues. I have tickets for the concert in the grotto, though I'm so nervous I barely hear the music.

Afterwards we eat hot chestnuts, bought from a man roasting them in a charcoal cart.

Lamps are lit and the avenues look romantic in the twinkling twilight. Some walks are not lit at all and I see couples disappearing down those to play hide and seek.

"Shall we walk a little?" I ask Anne.

"Yes, but not down those closed walks, they're too dark. Let's stay on the lighted ones."

I agree and she links arms with me. Does this mean she feels the same as me? I don't want this evening to stop. I have something to say but I don't know how to begin. Anne is silent too.

The moon is rising, large and golden, shining soft and round over a clear London sky. There are not many stars. I point the moon out to Anne and, as she turns to look, I slip my hand into my waistcoat pocket and pull out the small box.

"The moon is beautiful over the water, can you see its reflection?" She turns back to me. "Why, Ignatius, what are you doing down there?"

I am on bended knee beside her.

"My buckle is undone. One moment." I hide the box in my hand and look up at her. My heart is thumping.

"Anne, since I am down here, on one knee, would you do me the very great honour of becoming my wife?"

Now I show her the box in the palm of my hand and, opening it carefully, reveal a thin gold band set with small rubies and even smaller diamonds in a circle. I know the size is right because her brother helped me.

"Ignatius! It's beautiful!"

"Will you wear it, Anne? Will you wear my ring and spend the rest of your life with me?"

She pulls off her glove and holds out her hand.

"I will, Ignatius."

I stand up and put the ring on her fourth finger. We are both trembling with emotion. She has just made me the happiest man in the world.

Chapter 15

1767

Anne and I are soon married. We have three small children, all girls, Frances, Ann and Elizabeth. We call Elizabeth "Betsy", after the first person who stuck up for me. Although I haven't seen her again, Betsy will always be an important part of my life.

We move out of my rooms, which were far too small for all of us, and into a house. Though it is not long before that starts to feel too small for us as well. I wish we could move somewhere with plenty of space, but we cannot afford to. Not far from here there are brand-new fine houses with iron gates and airy courtyards which I know are built on the slave trade. My poor brothers and sisters work for nothing on sugar plantations so the houses' owners can grow rich and stir sugar into their tea. It makes me angry every time I walk past.

Still, we make the most of things. I love to go out walking with my family, and watch the little Sanchonettas run ahead.

We often come home by water taxi or carriage. Sometimes, people shout things at us on the street. They tell us that we need a wash so we'll turn white, or they bark orders at me and call me "Boy", even when I am twice their age. It always amazes me how some people make it their business to insult us because of our skin colour. I pity them, for there must be something lacking in their lives, to be so concerned by our passing by.

Early one evening later in the year, when London's streets are full of brown and orange leaves fallen from the trees, there is a knock at our front door.

"I'll get it!" says Anne, who has been helping me on with my coat.

"Whoever can it be?" I say. I'm getting ready to go out to one of our meetings.

Anne opens the door to a tall, thin Black man, a little younger than me.

"Why, hello, Francis," I say, as he comes in and bows to my wife. "You're early today! I was just on my way round to see you."

I usually knock on his door because in the past when I've waited for him to collect me, we're often late. He isn't very good at keeping time!

Francis Barber is a neighbour, and the valet to Dr Samuel

Johnson. I took him with me to one of our meetings and we have been going together ever since. Francis arrived in England from Jamaica, where he was enslaved, so he has a lot to tell us about the conditions over there.

"Are you ready?" he says. "Dr Johnson is waiting for us in his carriage. He's coming to our meeting today."

I am very fascinated by Dr Johnson, who published an amazing English dictionary a few years ago. It took him nine years to finish and now he is very famous. He wants to see an end to the slave trade too.

"Marvellous! Just a tick," I say, while Anne gives my coat a good brush across the shoulders with the clothes brush, so that it looks spick and span.

Our meetings are very informal. We listen to the latest information coming from the West Indies, or we hear about the lives of enslaved Africans in the North American colonies. The more we learn, the more I am convinced that freedom will come sooner rather than later. Tacky's War, in Jamaica, which came very close to people freeing themselves, has forced people in England to think about the system of slavery a lot more and start taking sides. We meet in coffee houses, or sometimes a hall if the meeting is going to be a special one, like tonight's. Our speaker is Mr Granville Sharp. We are going to hear all about a big success.

It's just as well we arrive early because the hall is already beginning to fill up. There are only two rows of chairs for older people to sit on. We make sure that Dr Johnson is comfortably seated before we go off to greet some of our friends who are gathering. Among them is John, Anne's brother.

"Marvellous news, isn't it?" he says, shaking my hand.

Soon it's standing room only. We give Granville Sharp a big cheer when he enters. Mr Sharp is a most marvellous Englishman who has become the father of our movement. He helped a sixteen-year old, Jonathan Strong, who was beaten up by his owner for running away. Sharp took the young man to hospital where he got better. Then Strong's owner wanted to enslave Strong all over again. Sharp made sure the Lord Mayor of London heard the case for Jonathan Strong's freedom.

We listen as Sharp tells us, "After a very heated debate the Lord Mayor said 'the lad had not stolen anything, and was not guilty of any offence, and was therefore at liberty to go away.'"

We cheer loudly. This news fills us with hope. It is the first time a former slave has challenged the law and won against his "owner".

The tide is turning and there will be an end to the slave

trade in my lifetime, I feel sure of it. Our movement is becoming stronger and more and more people are joining us once they understand how people are being forced to live. Even John Wesley, a clergyman who leads a group called the Methodists, has come out forcefully against the Trade. It can't be long now before it is stopped.

After the meetings there is always a discussion. The three of us, John, Francis and I, are sitting in a coffee house where another meeting has just finished. Most people have left but a few of us are still debating an idea that's been doing the rounds. Scooping up all the homeless Black people in London and sending them back to Africa. John doesn't think this is a good idea.

"Hardly anyone is sure what part of Africa they come from. No one has any family there that they know of. We don't even know our African names or languages. How would we cope?"

"It might be a chance for people with very few opportunities here to live in a new land,' says Francis. "They could start afresh. I, for one, am willing to think about it."

John leans forward. "But people would be left on their own, to fend for themselves. Or else have to work at something that would benefit England, rather than their own communities." We are all silent, thinking. He continues.

"The first wrong was to kidnap people and take them from their homes. It cannot be put right by forcing them to return, generations later. If people choose to go back to Africa, and have the means to do so, of course that is their right and wish. But this scheme of rounding up beggars worries me."

"Londoners are worried they are getting swamped by people from other parts of the world," I say.

"London has always been made up of many peoples, many classes and many shires. People come from the countryside to find work – some do, and some don't. Are we to ship all those unemployed back to Cornwall, or Lincolnshire, or Yorkshire?"

"Well, don't let's worry about it yet," I say. "You know how long it takes for politicians to do anything. They leave everything to the last minute."

John looks at me. "You need to write another one of your letters to the newspapers, Ignatius. Let the public know about what is being discussed, so there can be an open debate."

"You might be right, brother John. I shall write one of my letters, and I shall sign it Africanus, so they know it is from a man of Africa."

I have taken to writing to newspapers as part of our campaign to end the Trade.

Everyone is agreed on this though: no more kidnapping

of Africans and shipping them off to market! We will fight this and we will bring about change. It has to stop. I shall add my voice to the river. It is but a drop of water, but look how strong the river flows when it rains!

Chapter 16

Other than an end to the Trade, there is just one thing I don't have that would make my life better. Money. I'm finding it hard to pay the rent and put food on the table for my family. The old duchess left enough money for me to live comfortably on my own but, now there are five of us, it is no longer enough.

"We have some eggs left for tonight's supper," Anne says, "and John has sent some bread round for tomorrow's breakfast but, after that, I am not sure what we're going to eat."

I feel terrible. Especially as I went out last night and spent our last pennies watching David Garrick in his latest play.

"Oh dear," I say. "I didn't realize things were as bad as that."

"My brother is very kind and will make sure we don't starve, but I don't like to keep asking him. He has a family of his own to feed. We need to find a more long-lasting solution."

I know she's right. I sit in my armchair wondering what to do.

Anne has got up and walked to the window. I can hear the rumbling of carriages outside. Finally, she says, "Why don't you go and visit the new Duke and Duchess of Montagu? They might know of someone looking for staff."

I groan in protest. This idea has been at the back of my mind too but I don't like it.

"I feel that I shall be taking a step backwards, going into service again. You didn't marry a servant, but a gentleman."

Anne comes over and kneels down in front of me. "I married you, Ignatius, and I don't care if you're a tinker, a tailor, a soldier or a sailor. But, I'm sure you'll agree, we must be able to feed our children."

I notice for the first time that Anne is looking thin. And the children have colds. It's been a particularly hard winter. I stifle another sigh, and resign myself to doing what must be done.

The next morning finds me knocking on the side door of Montagu House. The old sign is still above the door, but everything has a new coat of paint. I only hesitate for a moment before lifting the heavy brass ring and knocking loudly.

William opens the door! I recognize him at once. His blonde hair is still thick but it has darkened. He looks as strong as ever.

"Sancho!" he exclaims. "How nice to see you!" He pumps my hand up and down. "Come through, come through," he says. "What can I do for you?"

I don't recognize any of the faces in the kitchen that look up curiously as he leads me to the little office that used to be mine.

"As you see, Sancho, your lessons made me realize that I wasn't stupid after all! And here I am, doing your old job! Now, sit down and tell me what you've been up to."

He beams at me. I sit down across the desk from him. He listens and nods thoughtfully as I bring him up to date with my life.

I walk up the grand staircase a few paces behind William and feel a pang of memory. The new duchess welcomes me in the drawing room. She is sitting on the sofa and the remains of a light breakfast are on a tray beside her. The duke is sitting in an armchair and all I can see is the top of his head poking up from behind the *London Gazette*.

The duchess listens to me politely, and I note her hairstyle is much bigger than her mother's more natural look. There are bows and ribbons in it –it is quite something – she must have got up early for her coiffeur to arrange all that.

My focus shifts suddenly to what she is saying. "But George needs a new valet! Don't you, George?"

George has only been half listening too, it seems, for he lowers the newspaper and looks over the top. "Do I? Yes! Yes, of course I do."

Soon after that I become the duke's valet. I organize his wardrobe, send his clothes to the laundry and make sure any mending is done promptly. I help him to dress in the mornings and also make travel arrangements if he wants to go anywhere. I make sure his day runs smoothly.

I am surprised to find I enjoy being in the Montagu household again. Anne is happier and the children are thriving. It is a big relief to be able to take care of my family duties and it is a joy to be in touch with William again.

Chapter 17

One morning, I find myself bowling through the English countryside, inside a post coach being pulled by a pair of nifty horses. We are on our way to Bath for the social season, along with all the other ladies and gentlemen of society. There will be shows, balls and dances in the assembly rooms. I enjoy this part of my job hugely.

There is a fair amount of jolting – the road is stony in parts and muddy in others – and the only means of stopping the coach is by controlling the horses. Even so, it is the best way to travel because it's private and you don't have to squash up with strangers.

"Why aren't we in one of those new coaches? I hear they are a lot more comfortable."

I am escorting two female servants and one of them complains every time there is a bump in the road.

The new public coaches to Bath are hung on steel springs

which make the journey a lot smoother. I look forward to travelling in one. I imagine there is more of a gentle swaying instead of the nonstop hammering on the ground.

The rolling hills are a green sea as we thud along. We forget about the lurching coach and tuck into a delicious goose pie that Cook packed for the journey. Anyone would think we haven't eaten for weeks. It must be the fresh country air that's making us hungry. My napkin is tucked into my neck cloth and flows down over my livery. I have to concentrate as the movement of the coach is very up and down. *Oops!* We nearly take a tumble, and I miss my mouth with the fork. The carriage jolts again and the ladies' feet go in the air as they hold on to each other. I land on the floor of the coach and can't get up! The ladies pull and push and finally I am in my seat again.

"Where is the goose?" I ask.

"It flew out of the window!" one of the ladies replies.

"Never to be seen again!" says the other.

"Thank goodness most of it is in my tummy then!" I say.

"How are we inside there?" the coachman booms down from his seat outside. "We come across a sudden attack of ditches, a proper storm of 'em. Must 'ave been raining a lot in these parts."

"All shipshape, thank you," I call back. "Only the goose has flown away."

Soon we are clattering over the river Avon into Bath and on to our lodgings. We have been sent ahead to make sure everything is in order for when the newly-weds arrive next week. I am referring to Elizabeth, daughter of the duchess, and her husband, Henry Scott. They haven't been married very long and this will be their first Season together. I think there's going to be a lot of fun ahead.

We settle into Bath. The city is growing very fast and practically all the buildings are made of the local, golden-coloured stone. It's very beautiful. Anne and the children have been able to join me and we rent some rooms near to the Montagu household where it's easy for me to come and go to work.

A very famous artist comes to paint a portrait of Her Grace, Lady Elizabeth. They are in the drawing room while I am arranging flowers in the dining room for a special dinner later this evening. A footman opens the door, walks over and whispers in my ear.

"Thomas Gainsborough wants to paint me?" I blurt out. The yellow rose I am holding falls to the dining table and lies among the broken stems and green leaves. "Are you saying the most famous artist in England, the best portrait painter, who has painted the Queen – has asked to paint *me*?"

"You better hurry up, he might change his mind!" the footman says.

"But I must return home, change my clothes, have a wash, goodness me, tell Anne! I must—"

"There isn't time. He wants to do it now, or not at all. You know how fast he works. It is now or never."

With that, I straighten my livery, pat my hair down and knock on the drawing room doors. I can only think that Mr Gainsborough saw me earlier, when I went in to help arrange Lady Elizabeth's dress for her portrait, and his curiosity was roused.

I can tell Mr Gainsborough is a very fussy man, with all his equipment neatly arranged. He is a flurry of hands, with many paintbrushes on the go at the same time. If I'm not mistaken, he is holding three of them in his mouth! Indeed, the portrait of Lady Elizabeth is almost done, he only has to finish off her clothes, which I think he will do back in his studio. She smiles at me when I enter and is about to say something, but Mr Gainsborough gets in first.

"Come," he says to me through the paintbrushes in his mouth. "Sit there. Now."

He points to a chair by the window. I scurry over, sit down. Lady Elizabeth wags her finger at me from behind her fan. She puckers her lips as if to say "Shhh!" and sweeps out.

Mr Gainsborough bows at her departing figure and then turns to me. "Look over there," he barks.

And for the next hour and forty minutes, to be precise, I am left to my musings and Mr Gainsborough to his paints.

There is a reason why his interest may have been piqued. I have become quite famous! Not only have my newspaper letters been read widely but so have my private letters with Laurence Sterne, whose writing I have enjoyed for years. Laurence was a stranger to me when I wrote my first letter, but I felt he was someone who cared about humanity. I can't remember my exact words, but I remember my letter asked him to include a Black person in his next story, to bring attention to the Trade. To be honest, I was amazed he replied. I've written many letters to famous people and hardly anyone does. He said that, funnily enough, he had just finished a story about a friendless Black girl when my letter arrived. He was very interested in how things were going with the anti-slave trade movement. We met up and became friends, writing to each other quite often after that.

After his sad death last year, our letters were published, along with his other papers and suddenly everyone knew who I was! I am pleased that our letters are now used to help our campaign. We shall succeed – we must – even though it's taking longer than I first imagined.

Sitting for a portrait can put you in a trance. My eyes become vacant, even close once or twice, for the fire is roaring and the last of the sun's rays are filtering through the window. I keep myself occupied by making up a melody which I sing in my head. It is a lively little piece. I must remember it, as there is a Montagu Ball next week and Lady Elizabeth has asked me to compose some dance tunes for it. I find myself humming out loud. Mr Gainsborough doesn't seem to mind so I continue, adding flourishes here and there.

"I have no objection to the melody, but you are twitching!"

Mr Gainsborough's paintbrushes do not stop. I apologize and try to keep my mouth and toes in order.

At last, he is finished. His skill is quite remarkable. Here I am, in the flesh, and there I am, perched on his easel, oil-painted on a canvas. He has caught me very well, even the half-smile when he asked me to sit still.

Chapter 18

1774

As the years go by, it becomes harder and harder to fulfil my duties. I find it difficult to get about as quickly as I used to, and there is a lot of getting about when you are the valet to a duke. The stairs are the worst – upstairs, downstairs, front stairs, back stairs – my poor knees are giving up. Also, a valet needs to attend his master when he goes out in his carriage and so I find there is very little free time for myself.

Finally, the duke and I have a conversation about my difficulties.

"What you need, Sancho, is a different profession!"

We discuss the problem this way and we discuss the problem that way and the solution is: I am now a grocer!

The duke helps me to buy a shop in Charles Street, Westminster, where I sell sugar, tea and tobacco. It is a perfect location as there are lots of families in the area that need a local shop, as well as politicians who pass by on their way to

Parliament. The duke sends his servants to buy from me, and many of his friends buy from me too. Anne and the girls help me to run the shop and so, as well as spending more time together, I have more time to spend on my letters and the things dear to my heart. I am such a lucky man!

I am always the first one up. Old habits die hard as the saying goes. I love these October mornings. Sometimes the sky is a wash of red, streaked with golden clouds as the sun announces the beginning of another day. I lie awake for a few minutes and count my blessings, giving thanks for them, especially for my family. Anne is expecting another baby. I bless her and all our children.

Then I tiptoe downstairs, as best a big man can, and stoke the embers of the kitchen range, pile on more wood and put the kettle on to boil. It is my delight to bring my wife her cup of tea every morning – one lump of sugar and a dash of milk on a little tray, much as I did for the sisters, all those years ago in Greenwich. But now my heart is filled with love. Anne does so much for me and our family.

"Why don't you take a day off today, Anne? I can manage the shop. You need to rest."

She smiles up at me and I leave her quietly sipping.

I open the shutters at the front. It's a beautiful day. The kind when the sun shows every speck of dust on the windowpanes. "Clean me!" they are saying. I do the insides first, wetting the windowpane and wiping my cloth all over, making sure all the corners get done. Then I dry and polish them.

"Now for the outside," I say to myself, sloshing the dirty water into the street. Once I've fetched some fresh water and wiped the windows they start to sparkle.

My friend Francis Barber comes walking down the street. He has with him a young Black man I'm sure I've seen somewhere before, who he introduces as Ottobah Cugoano. I put down the dirty cloth and wipe my hands on my apron before greeting them both.

"I believe I've seen you at a meeting recently?" I say to Ottobah.

Ottobah bows. "Yes, indeed. I heard about the meetings and wanted to come and see for myself."

"Ottobah was captured when he was thirteen," says Francis. "Like me, he spent time suffering under slavery in the West Indies. Ottobah is now working for Mr Richard Cosway, around the corner."

"I am sorry to hear of your sufferings, brother," I say to him. "You're very welcome at the meetings, Ottobah, anytime." I sigh. "I thought our work would be done by now, but it's not. It's good to see young people taking up the battle."

Then I turn to Francis. "And how is Doctor Johnson these days? I hear he's not doing so well."

"I don't know what's the matter with him. He doesn't even want to get dressed some mornings. Are you open yet?"

"You can be my first customer of the day, Francis, and bring me luck."

"You missed a bit," he says, pointing to a dry patch in the corner of a windowpane.

"I haven't finished yet," I say, ushering them inside. I know he's only teasing.

"Actually, we've come to ask you about yesterday," Francis says, pushing his list over the shop counter that I've gone to stand behind. "Voting in the election – how did it go?"

"It passed without any incident."

"Go on, we want to know every detail."

"Well, I stood in line – " I begin, glancing at his shopping list and reaching for a pouch of tobacco. I put it on the counter before reading the next item, a packet of tea – "I gave my name and occupation and then an officer wrote down who I was voting for. As you know, voting isn't private, anyone can see who you vote for."

"What did the officer write down about you?" asks Ottobah.

"Only that I am a tea dealer, and I live in the parish of St Margaret's, Westminster."

Francis and Ottobah ask me all sorts of questions, about how long it took and who else was standing in the line. There were other householders – cheesemongers, tailors, bricklayers, gentlemen, booksellers – a wide variety, I tell them.

"With two things in common," says Ottobah.

"Hah, yes," I agree. "All male and all owning a house."

"Exactly. It's only because you own number 19, Charles Street, that you're allowed to vote."

"And did you stand out in any way?" Ottobah says. I'm not quite sure what he's getting at.

"What do you mean?"

Ottobah looks at me. "Were there any other Black men?"

"No, none." This has not occurred to me before.

"You know what this means, Ignatius? You are the first African man in England – ever – to vote." Ottobah is looking at me seriously. Francis is beaming.

"Who, me?" I say. "The first *ever*?"

They both nod. I have to sit down. Imagine, me, the little boy who slaved for the sisters and had to fight so hard to be able to read and write, has become the first Black man to have a say in who governs England.

"How does it feel, my friend?" asks Francis.

"It feels important."

"It is. You are the first—"

"—And not the last, I hope," I say, standing up, feeling suddenly stronger.

They both shake my hand and clap me on the back.

"You must continue writing to newspapers, Ignatius, expressing your opinion, sharing your thoughts," says Ottobah. I look at him, this serious young man with his sharp, clever eyes.

"I write letters, Ottobah, but you can write a book. John Wesley has written his *Thoughts on Slavery*, but you have lived through it. Write your own book, telling of your capture and the horrors our brothers and sisters have to endure. The trading of Africans has to stop."

Ottobah frowns, and I can see the idea taking root. "My book shall not only call for the end of the Trade, but for the end of slavery itself."

"Yes, it will."

PART 3

PROJECTING MY VOICE

1780

Chapter 19

The years pass, and business booms. Customers come each morning; their faces and their shopping lists grow familiar to me. In the afternoons, friends pop by to ask my opinion about a painting they are working on or a book they are reading. But by 1780, the shop is not as busy as it once was. Britain seems to be at war with most of its neighbours. The American colonies are fighting for their independence, too. Because it is harder to get goods into the country, prices are higher, wages are lower and many have lost their jobs. People don't seem to have so much money to spend.

To make matters worse, a march on Parliament is happening this morning, and I worry it will lead to a mob. The march is in protest of a new law, called the Papists Act, which gives Catholics more liberties. Some of the marchers are Protestants and are against the Catholic way of life. But for many people out today, marching is just a way to show their frustration about the lack of jobs or the sad state of the country's economy. I am staring out the window, wondering whether thousands of feet will soon be stomping down the peaceful street, when Ottobah comes into the shop. Thank goodness for loyal customers!

"That man Gordon is stirring up trouble," Ottobah says, once he has read out his shopping list. Lord George Gordon is one of the loudest voices against the new law. If he is out today, that doesn't bode well for a peaceful march. "He is exciting the crowd against Catholics and it will end badly. Nobody can control a mob. And there's about fifty thousand people gathered..." He shakes his head. "Add a pouch of your finest snuff and then I'll be off. I don't want to be out on the streets today."

"Why are people always arguing is what I want to know. Why can't we all live together peacefully?" I sigh as I walk with him to the door.

I watch him walking down the street and glance both ways before closing the shop door. We are living in difficult times.

I hear a thump and very soon a little head appears around the door behind the counter. It is Billy, my youngest, who I named William after my friend at the Montagus.

"Morning, Papa. Can I go out and play with my hoop?"

"Not today, Billy. And must you always jump the last few steps of the stairs? It worries your mother."

"But how will I get good at jumping if I don't practise?" Billy says, climbing on to the counter and jumping off it to land at my feet.

"Did you do your studies yesterday, Billy?"

He looks at me and shakes his head.

"Well, how will you get good at reading and writing if you don't practise?" I say, feeling rather pleased with myself.

"I'm hungry," Billy says. "Can I have some porridge?"

"You may, but please do not change the subject."

Billy fetches his slate and slate pencil from underneath the shop counter.

"Now, write me out your alphabet in your best handwriting," I say. "See how many letters you can fit on the slate."

My oldest daughter, Frances, comes in. She is nineteen now. Billy is bent over his slate and has reached the letter "D, d".

"Are you sure that's the way 'd' looks, Billy?" she says, looking over his shoulder. He stares at it and then licks his finger seriously, rubs out the straight line and puts it on the other side of the curve. He looks up at her.

"That's better."

She goes over to the sugar cones that came in yesterday with my order of tobacco and starts unpacking them, counting them off as she goes.

"Your mind needs equipment just as cooks need their pots and pans, Billy," I say on my way to the kitchen. "Would you like some porridge too, Frances?"

She is so wrapped up counting she doesn't answer me. I head to the kitchen, make two bowls of steaming cinnamon porridge, and then return to the shop.

"Here we are," I say, placing them on the counter. "I made some for you anyway, Frances. I'll have it if you don't want it." I look around. "Where's Billy?"

"Beg pardon, Papa?"

"I said where's Billy? Did he go back upstairs?"

Frances looks up from her work. "He's right here ... Oh, where's he gone?"

I turn back and shout his name up the stairs.

"He's not up here," Anne calls back.

"I hope he's not outside," I say. "There's a march on Parliament this morning."

Frances and I hurry to open the front door. There are quite a few children out there, running with their hoops, skipping, or playing tag.

"I can't see Billy," Frances says. "And what's that rumble?"

"It sounds like the crowd coming this way." I raise my voice. "Children! Go home! Go inside!"

There is no knowing what a lot of excited people will do. Some children look at me with questions on their faces. Then one hears the rumble of the mob. He drops his hoop and runs to his house. Soon children are running in every direction, leaving hoops and skipping ropes scattered on the ground. I still can't see my son.

"William!" I shout. He knows I mean business when I use his full name.

There is no answer. I change tactics.

"Billy? Billy, where are you? This is not the time to play hide and seek! Come out at once!"

I'm in the street now, looking up and down. Anne has joined Frances by the door.

A young lad calls out to me, as his father is bundling him inside. "I saw him, Mr Sancho. He was knocking at number nine."

"When was that, Jacob?" I shout, hurrying over but all I can hear is, "About..." as he is pulled inside. I can't catch what he says and his voice fades behind the closed door.

"I'll fetch him, Papa," says Frances, ducking out from behind her mother, no doubt feeling guilty for letting him out of her sight. Billy is only five years old after all.

"There isn't time," I say, scurrying back across the road to prevent her disappearing down the street. "He'll be safe with the Millers at number nine."

Just then the crowd turns on to Charles Street. I push Anne and Frances into the shop and shut the door. The noise of hundreds of people shouting is like a wave crashing over the houses. I am not afraid for myself and stand alone, outside the door of the shop, to watch. The crowd swells towards me and I see people at the front holding up large banners. One reads "The Protestant Association" and another "Repeal the Papists Act!".

An open carriage approaches from the other end of the street. It appears someone has timed their journey home very badly. As the carriage meets the crowd I see its occupant swiping at people with his swordstick. The crowd swarms over him like wasps, pulling him from his carriage and giving him a few good thumps in return before tossing him aside. He stumbles towards his house. The door opens and swiftly closes once he is safely in.

Thousands of men swearing and swaggering down the street armed with large sticks are not to be crossed, I decide. Talking to them in this mood would be pointless so I come inside myself. Now is not the time for a discussion.

Chapter 20

That is a lot of unhappy people, I think as I bolt the door.
I turn and see that Anne has gathered our other two
girls into the shop as well. All four of them are sitting on
straight-backed chairs, drinking hot chocolate.

"Hot chocolate in June?" I say.

"Hush, it's comforting," she says, passing me a cup, too.
It's true, it is comforting. My girls are scared and so is Anne.
She stands over by the window, peeping out, in case she
sees Billy.

"If that boy has any sense, he'll lie low until this mob has
passed," I say, bringing her back to the chairs.

"You're right, he will come home safe once the crowd has
moved on."

She sits down, torn between worry and not wanting to
scare her daughters.

The girls are staring out of the window too, as if looking

hard enough can make the mob vanish and Billy appear safe and sound.

"Shall I tell you how we came to own this shop?" I say, hoping to distract them. They make no reply.

"It's a long story and you will have to listen carefully. And come closer, for I don't want to shout. There is quite enough of that going on outside."

This raises a smile from Betsy and I am encouraged.

"Now, where to begin? Ah yes … Betsy, you were around Billy's age when we got this shop. It's easy to say, 'Why don't we open a shop?' It was much harder to make happen. We needed to count our pennies very carefully if we were to afford it. We needed money to live every day, as well as money to buy goods to stock up the shop. The duke helped us, of course, but there was a lot we had to do on our own. One night – do you remember, Anne? – we sat up and made a list of what had to happen to make our dream come true."

"Yes," Anne says, sitting on the chair beside me and counting off on her fingers, "One, buy a property. Two, buy provisions. Three, sell provisions."

I smile. "Put like that it all sounds easy, but to buy a property we needed to look for the right kind of building, in the right kind of place, and so it went on."

"We decided to sell all the little things our neighbours

needed on a daily basis," Anne chips in. "That was our motto."

"And it still is today, seven years later. Look around you and tell me what you see on the shelves."

Frances smiles. She doesn't need to look around as she works in the shop. Neither does Ann, our seventeen-year-old who is named after her mother. (Though, as she often reminds us, her name is spelled differently.) But Betsy turns her head and looks this way and that.

"I see tea, tobacco and sugar," she says.

"Aye. And soap, starch, figs and raisins," agrees Frances.

I glance at Anne and she smiles at me. It's working, our girls are feeling less worried.

"We had to cut our coat according to our means, which were slender," I say, "and expand as we went along. Rather like me! I was a slender boy but, oh my goodness, instead of one chin I now have two, as good Mr Gainsborough painted, rather too truthfully in my portrait."

I laugh comfortably. "But, thankfully, my teeth are my own and I am strong. There are men more handsome than I, I have to admit, but I am content with my looks and pleased that those who love me do so for who I am and not how I appear. A smile is worth a thousand pearls in my eyes."

My wife pats my bad knee tenderly. I try not to wince, as it hurts most of the time, but I don't want to worry her.

Ann stands up and collects our cups. She puts them on the shop counter and reaches for her apron.

"What are you doing, my little Sanchonetta?" I ask.

"I thought I'd cut up some of those sugar cones," she says, reaching for the sugar nippers.

"I'll help you," says Betsy and she jumps up. I protest but Anne holds my arm.

"Let them," she says quietly. "It'll keep their minds off things outside."

"Well, be careful," I say. "Those cutters are sharp and that sugar is as hard as hard can be."

I have lost half my audience! Ann is old enough to manage the nippers and Betsy gathers up the cut sugar and puts the lumps in a large glass jar.

I imagine Billy sitting in the house a few doors away with his friend, perhaps playing in the back room. I say this out loud and then add, "I will go round there as soon as the mob moves on and bring him home."

I look out of the window and see that it has started raining. "This will stop the party," I say.

Chapter 21

By the time the rain peters out, it seems that the crowd has indeed moved on. More importantly, it has not come back. Anne helps me to change into my jacket. I dare not leave it any longer for, although it's summer, the light outside is beginning to fade.

"Bring him back, you hear?" Anne says.

"I expect he'll be hungry when he gets in," I say. "Why not go and make something for him to eat?"

"Already done," she says, as she watches me lift the bolt from across the front door. I'm not looking forward to going out. I'm afraid of what I'll see. Suddenly, there is a loud banging on the outside of the door.

"Stay there! Don't move!" Anne commands. She goes over to the window and peeps out.

"Open it! Oh, open it! Billy is brought home!"

I lift the latch and an arrow of a little boy races into his mother's arms and they hug each other tight. I am not sure which one is crying the most. There is another figure by the front door who hangs back. It is not Mr Miller.

"Come in," I say. "Any stranger who brings our boy back to us is most welcome in my home."

A tall, thick-set white man steps over the threshold. He looks clumsy and strong. His face is streaked with soot and his clothes are dripping on to the shop floor. Billy lets go of his mother and, wiping his nose on his sleeve, says, "Please may I present Pike, who has been so kind as to look after me all day."

I am so amazed at Billy's good manners that I forget my own. "What? I thought you were at number nine?"

"I was, Papa, at first, but I wanted to come home. They tried to keep me in but I slipped out as they were closing the door and, although they called for me to come back, I got swept along in the crowd and couldn't. Then, when I reached our door, I called out – but no one heard."

When he says these last words Billy bursts into tears again.

"Oh Billy, Billy, there, there," Anne says. "You're home now."

"I saw the boy," Pike takes over, "trying to fight his way against the crowd but it swept him along. I scooped him up, setting him on my shoulders, so he wouldn't get trampled. I noted where we were. 'Don't worry, lad,' I says. 'We'll come back as soon as we can. You're with me, Pike, and I keeps my promises.'"

"Mr Pike, we are greatly in your debt," I say. "Stay and refresh yourself, you must be hungry and exhausted. And my goodness, you're wet through."

"Yes, yes, of course," Anne says, still hugging Billy. "We can't thank you enough for bringing our little boy home."

"Pike will do, and thankee, I am hungry as it happens," he says. "To be honest, Ma'am, I should be thanking Billy. Because he was with me, I didn't do no silly things. Lord knows where I'd be now if I hadn't scooped him up. He saved me from myself."

The man sways and holds on to the back of a chair.

"Frances, take that wet coat and put it by the fire in the back room," I say. "We shall hear about your adventures when you have eaten. After you, Pike, after you." I usher him ahead of me into the dining room.

Frances brings in a bowl of clean water and a towel. Pike gives his face and hands a thorough wash. Betsy has taken Billy into the kitchen and is no doubt doing the same for him. I can see now Pike's face is crinkled and weather-beaten, as though he spends a lot of time out of doors.

Ann and her mother bring in dishes of cold ham and turkey, boiled eggs, bread and cheese. There is quiet as Pike and Billy tuck into the food. We all watch them, our questions locked silently on to our tongues.

Finally, Billy says, his mouth half full of bread, "I saw everything from Pike's shoulders, Papa. The flames went all the way up to heaven."

"Goodness gracious, son, where were you?" Anne says in alarm.

"I don't know, Mama, but the fires were hot and cinders were flying in the air."

I look over at Pike, my eyebrows raised.

"We were swept along to the City. It was like being on a river – there was no going against the flow. We ended up outside Newgate Prison. The mob broke down the doors, let the prisoners out and then set fire to the buildings. We sheltered in a doorway and watched from there. The smoke was something terrible. When the crowd moved on we stayed behind. And here we are. We've seen somethings to remember, ain't we, Billy boy?"

I don't like to ask Pike why he was in such a crowd, but he sees the question on my face for he carries on. "There was no work on today, so when I sees a great crowd marching, I joins it. See if I get any breaks."

"I will, of course, reward you for your kind service to us today. Although I cannot repay you as much as you deserve."

Pike scrapes his chair back and stands up. "You mistake me, Sir. I didn't rescue your lad to earn a reward. I have a lad myself, waiting for me at home. Now, I have kept my promise and you must excuse me."

He turns to leave. I stand up too.

"Sorry, Pike, I didn't mean to offend you. Please, sit down again. I was only saying the first thing that came into my head. I would like to give you a hundred thousand guineas, but of course I can't. What you did was priceless. I was trying to express my gratitude."

The man pauses before giving a brief nod and sitting down again.

"Where do you live?" I say with relief.

"Lincoln. I came to London to look for work but it has been hard to find. Just the odd job here and there, labouring on the new roads, breaking stones and such. But I shall set off home directly. There is no steady work and today has shown me where I need to be. At home, with my family."

"I'm sure they will be very pleased to see you. They will have missed you," Anne says.

Pike looks at her, "Thank you, Ma'am," he says. "I know

what I have now and I don't want to lose it. There isn't much work in Lincoln, same as London, but I have a small piece of land there, which we grow our food on. We have chickens aplenty so there are eggs too. It's not much, but it's home."

"I will make a parcel of food for your journey. It will take you a good few days."

"It took five days to get here so I expect the same, maybe longer, after what's happened."

"Rest a while, won't you?" I say. I look over at Billy but he has disappeared. My heart skips a beat. "Where's Billy? Where's that boy gone now?"

It doesn't take long to find him. He has fallen asleep and slipped off his chair. We find him in a little heap under the table. Pike lifts him up and places him on his mother's lap. Billy wiggles and tries to get comfortable.

"Thank you, but I better set off now," Pike says. "London's in chaos and the trouble will spread. I won't get very far once the soldiers are called out to deal with the mobs."

Frances takes Billy in her arms and she and Betsy go upstairs to put him in bed. Ann helps her mother make up a parcel of food for Pike. I go into the shop and come back with a packet of tea and some of the sugar lumps Ann cut earlier.

"This is for you, Pike. It's a present, not a reward. You and your kind heart will always be welcome here if you pass this way again. We shall never forget you."

Pike accepts the presents and the food parcel. "Say goodbye to Billy for me," he says.

We shake hands and the whole family waves Pike goodbye as he sets off on his journey home. All except Billy, who is safely tucked up in bed.

Chapter 22

After a week, the mobs are all gone. The soldiers put the fires out and round up most of the ringleaders. London soon stops talking about this excitement, but it takes longer for Billy to forget. I sit with him every night until he falls asleep. One night, as Billy is snuggling down in our bed – we are all spoiling him a bit – he looks at me with wide eyes.

"I was scared, Papa."

I am sitting beside him on the bed. "Of course you were. Scary things were happening."

"Yes, but I wasn't even a little bit brave."

"There are times when the best course of action is to run away."

"Really?" Billy says, sitting up and hugging his knees. "There were so many people, we couldn't run anywhere. We were stuck."

"Just so."

Billy looks at me. "I wanted an adventure, Papa. Nothing ever happens around here."

"There's a lot to be said for a quiet life, Billy my boy," I say.

Billy throws himself back down in the bed and groans. "You would say that, Papa, you just want to stay home and let the same thing happen day after day."

This stops me for a moment. "I knew a boy once," I say, "who had a lot of adventures."

"Tell me about him, please. What was his name?"

"Let's just call him Boy because, in truth, he was called that many times all through his life, even after he had grown into a man."

Billy sits up again, arranging the pillow behind his head. He looks at me and nods, as if to say, carry on.

"This little boy didn't have to go to war, but he did have to fight battles every day."

"Battles, Papa?"

"People thought he was stupid because he couldn't read or write. And when everyone keeps telling you you're stupid it's hard not to believe that yourself. People said it would be far better for him, and the world, if he didn't know anything, so he could do all the mindless jobs that needed doing."

"Like what?"

"You do ask a lot of questions, Billy! Like sweeping the

same floor every day for twenty years. These people said he was too stupid to enjoy music, or a good play."

"I wish I knew this little boy," Billy says.

"Do you, Billy?"

"Yes."

"Why is that?"

Billy looks thoughtful. "I would be his friend and tell him not to worry what other people think. I would help him with his a, b, c."

"That is very kind of you, Billy. It would have been nice for him to have had a friend."

I need to blow my nose just then. Billy snuggles into the pillow.

"Let's join this boy when he is not quite a man. Shall we do that, Billy?"

"Yes, if that is a good place to start." He yawns and gets comfortable.

"It is, son, for he makes a decision that will change his whole life."

"And what is that, Papa?" Billy says sleepily.

"He decides to run away."

"Why, what from?"

"Because he is sad and very scared. Shall I paint the scene for you, Billy?"

He blinks hard and says, "Mmm." His eyelids droop a little. "It happened like this ..."

I stuff my handkerchief into my pocket and when I look down at Billy, he is not looking up at me any more. He is fast asleep. I'm glad. I want to give him the best, the very best, start in life. How can I do this? Not through money, there is very little of that in my purse. More would be welcome, but gathering money is not the best route to happiness.

I want him to understand there is always a choice in life, that he can choose a life for himself. He is a lively little boy, full of questions, and that is good. All the learning I wish for Billy, I wish for my daughters too. It is just as important for them to learn and be interested in life. I tuck him up and kiss his forehead before snuffing out the candle and tiptoeing out of the room.

Over the next few days, Billy asks to hear more about the boy. When I tell the story of when the boy stole the biscuits, I see that it had been a trap all along. I realize that the sisters must have left the biscuits out to tempt me into doing something bad. Billy doesn't like this story. As I sit quietly, remembering my shame, he runs over, climbs on to my lap and throws his arms around my neck.

Chapter 23

One night, as rain thuds down on the roof, I hold the banister to help me upstairs into the attic, where my study is. Anne finds me there half an hour later, rummaging through a wooden chest, humming a little tune.

"My goodness, whatever are you doing, Mr Sancho?"

"I'm looking for – for – ah, there they are!"

I pick up a bundle of letters, tied with string and stamped with sealing wax. The letters are brown with age. I clasp them to me, like long lost friends.

"Help me up, Anne," I say. She puts her candle on the desk and helps me into an armchair, moving a footstool so I can prop my bad leg up. She sits on the straight-backed chair by the desk.

"What do you have in your hand?" she asks.

"All those years ago, while I was working at the Montagus, and after the old duchess died – when I was a free man – I practised writing letters to myself. I never threw them away, thinking one day I might like to read them. Looking at Billy just now reminded me."

"You funny man. I'd love to hear one," Anne says.

I untie the string, fan the letters out and invite Anne to pick one, as if she is choosing a magician's card. She gives me the one she has chosen and I break the seal, unfold it, clear my throat theatrically. She laughs, and I begin.

"Ignatius, dear chap, this will not do. Lying among the sheets, however wet and miserable outside, will not make your fortune. It is past noon and you were still in bed up to ten minutes ago.

It's true, the rain outside has got the better of me. I gave in to the warm blankets. But I did peep out from beneath, bedcap askew, and threw a quilt about my shoulders. I got as far as my desk, whereupon I sharpened a few quills to pen this epistle ..."

"Very high flown! 'Epistle!'" says Anne.

"Thank you," I say. "I was practising."

"There is no reason why I should dirty clean clothes at this time of the day. Far better to keep them fresh for this evening, when I am off to see Mr Garrick perform his Hamlet. I can think of no better way of waving my last pennies goodbye.

And so – back to bed! I promise not to eat my lunch in

it. Crumbs or soup stains are not to be found in a bed – they encourage visits from furry friends. "Get thee hence!" I have been heard to shout more than once, followed by a tossed boot or bowl, whichever is nearest to hand. How I hate being poor! But I hate to miss this Hamlet even more. Aha! I am a poet! I must feed my soul, as well as my body, but NOT IN BED.

And so farewell, my Sancho. I wish you Godspeed upon your journey through life. I hope I find a Penny Mountain soon, and find the love of a good woman (please God let it be Anne).

Yours in affectionate camaraderie, Ignatius Sancho

P.S. The rain is lashing the windowpanes. I shall need to consider different shoes if it does not stop before this evening's show. My last pennies need to be enjoyed to the maximus and this won't happen with wet feet."

I stop and look at Anne. She is wiping tears of laughter from her cheeks.

"How sensible you were even then," she says.

"How lucky I was that you agreed to be my bride and life's companion," I say. "You are my foundation, my comfort, my love, the treasure of my soul."

"And you are mine, Ignatius," she says, getting up. "Come to bed now."

"In a minute, my dear."

With that Anne leaves me. I hear her soft tread going back down the stairs.

The little boy I was is still inside the man I am now. He has learned so much over the years – that being someone's servant does not stop a person from becoming who they want to be. I hope Don Quixote's Sancho is pleased with me. I use his name with pride.

It is not for someone else to decide what you can do. I'm glad I ran away from the sisters in Greenwich. I might still be there, still serving them breakfast, still trying to persuade them to allow me to learn. I should probably have given that up by now. I'm glad I took part in my life and didn't just wait for something to happen.

I pick up my quill, sharpen it, dip it in ink, bring out a fresh sheet of paper.

"*Dear Boy,*" I write, but stop, pass the feathered end of the quill back and forth under my nose. That's not right. It might not only be a boy that reads this – look at how clever *all* my Sanchonettas are. I scratch out "*Boy*" and am about to write "*Girl*" when the feather stops again. I dip the nib in ink and write "*P-e-r-s-o-n*".

Of course! For that they are – a person! That is much better, only now there is a blob of ink as well after I write the "*n*". No matter, "*Dear Person*" it is.

Dear ~~Boy~~ Person,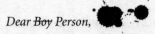

You will be reading this perhaps hundreds of years after I write. It's exciting to know you can read (sorry about the messy handwriting) and that you are reading MY WORDS. Now I've got over the excitement of imagining you, I'm wondering what to say!

Mutatis mutandis *comes to mind and, before you start asking what it means, I'll tell you. It's Latin, and it means what needs to be changed, has been changed. I do so hope that's true. Why not make a list of things that have changed since my life and yours?*

Take part in your life, don't sit around waiting for it to happen. Start preparing now for what you want to happen when you are older. Nothing you do will be wasted, believe me. I went from being enslaved to being able to vote. I am a man of letters! I have always done my best and not been too proud to accept help when it's offered. Every day is a new beginning.

The Trade has still not been abolished. It has grown bigger, in fact. I was so sure it would have ended by now. But the people with the power to end it are the same people making money from it. Still, we mustn't give up. The Trade will end. We just have to keep bringing its shame to people's attention.

I hope reading and writing is something you enjoy.
It can be a way of expressing how you feel and what you
think. I hope the world is ready to hear your thoughts
and feelings, and that you are open to hearing the
thoughts and feelings of others. Stories come in all
shapes and sizes and you will enjoy some more than
others. Listen to them all. Some will teach you things
and other people will learn from your stories, so long as
you express yourself honestly.

I wasn't allowed to learn for the longest time. I hope
this is not the case for you. Learning helps a person
think, and thinking helps to learn. It is possible to teach
yourself many things, no matter what age you are, so
please don't give up. Sometimes it takes one person
longer than someone else. That is to be expected and
doesn't matter. How quickly or slowly a person learns
has nothing to do with how a person goes on to use what
they've learned. There is no "best age". You can learn at
any time in your life, and in any way you choose. All
that is required is you have to want to. It changed my
life for the better. I recommend it to you.

Let me share something I wrote to a friend: I would
not give you money, or land, or horses or camels, nor the
most excellent elephants. I would give you BOOKS.

Know your own worth and honour yourself – not
with snooty pride – but with the confidence of your own
true merit.

With all best wishes for a happy and enjoyable life.
Your friend,
Ignatius Sancho

I pick up the candle, look back at my letter to a future person and close the door quietly behind me.

Author's Note

Ignatius Sancho left us something rare and precious – his voice. As a Black man living nearly three hundred years ago, he wrote to newspapers about things he cared about, such as ending the slave trade. He also wrote personal letters to his friends, meant just for them, so we know the letters are a true reflection of how he really felt. When these letters were collected and published in a book two years after his death, the book sold out immediately.

Characters

Some of the characters in this book are fictional, including Betsy the maid-of-all-work, Brydges the butler, William the footman and Pike, the labourer who saves Billy. However, it is likely Ignatius Sancho would have come across people just like them. The duke and duchess and their family, Sancho's wife and children and most of his friends were all real people, though I have imagined some of the scenes in their lives.

Anne Osborne, Sancho's wife, could read and write too. Their marriage was a happy one and they had seven children, though sadly three of them died very young. Their son, William (Billy in our story), turned the shop in Charles Street into a publishing house and became the first Black publisher in Britain.

Ottobah Cugoano really did go on to write a book. He called it *Thoughts and Sentiments on the Evils and Wicked Traffic of the Slavery and Commerce of the Human Species.*

You could research other people mentioned in this book and see what you can find out about them!

Eighteenth Century London

At the time this story is set, London was beginning to look like it does now. The Great Fire of London in 1666 destroyed a large number of London's wooden buildings and narrow alleys. New buildings went up, now made of stone to withstand accidental fire. Streets were widened and bridges built across the Thames. London grew westwards as the wind mostly blew from that direction. It meant that the smells of industry and manufacturing were carried eastwards and away from the new houses of Westminster and Mayfair.

London was a very busy place. New banks opened, lending money to plantation owners in the West Indies, the American colonies and in the East. Bankers conducted their business in coffee houses and from their wealthy mansions.

Frost fairs on the Thames, like the one Ignatius and Betsy went to, haven't happened since the old London Bridge was pulled down and a new one built in 1831. The new bridge has fewer arches which means more salt water can flow upriver (salty water has a lower freezing point to fresh water). Also, after embankments were built to contain the river on both sides, it flows faster, giving ice less chance to form. The last time the Thames froze in London was 1814.

Ocean-going ships came all the way up the Thames to Tilbury docks. Trading companies, such as the Royal African Company, brought sugar and tobacco to the capital. This made Royal African Company owners and merchants rich. The Royal African Company was responsible for shipping more Africans to the West Indies than any other company. The East India Company brought tea, silks, new foods and spices to England and made their merchants very rich as well.

Eighteenth Century Bath

Ever since Queen Anne visited Bath in 1703 to take the waters for her health, a social scene developed in the town. By the time Ignatius Sancho visited in 1767 it was a very popular place.

Lady Elizabeth Montagu, Duchess of Buccleuch and Queensbury, had her portrait painted by the artist, Thomas Gainsborough, in 1767, probably at the same time Ignatius Sancho had his picture painted. His portrait now hangs in the National Gallery of Canada.

Roads and Travel

To carry all the new goods up and down the country, Britain's roads needed to improve. Coaches often overturned due to the bad road conditions and it was easy for highwaymen to rob travellers. For example, on 4 October, 1774, Lord North – the prime minister – was held up and robbed near Chiswick. If highwaymen were caught, however, they were hanged.

The Age of Enlightenment

The mid-eighteenth century saw the beginning of what is known as the Age of Enlightenment. Many new philosophers and poets started thinking in different ways to the past.

Granville Sharp, who appears briefly in our story, was born in Durham before moving to London. He loved music and singing. To his friends he signed off his letters as G# (like the musical note, G-sharp). Sharp was involved in winning freedom for Jonathan Strong (who appears in our story). After that he fought many legal battles for social justice.

War and Revolution

Britain was involved in several wars during Ignatius Sancho's lifetime. Wars are expensive for countries so, while individuals may have enriched themselves, the country was in debt. The Seven Years' War with France, between 1756 and 1763, was a struggle for power in the "New World", the name given to the Americas and the West Indian islands at the time. A lot of Europeans went to the New World and settled there. These colonies, as they were called, were part of the Spanish, French or British Empires.

At the end of the war, France and Britain divided up large parts of the New World for themselves, which brought wealth to their countries and saw the end of the Spanish Empire.

The British king, George III, wanted his colonies in America to pay for the British war with the French, but they didn't agree. They quarrelled for many years. King George III's government kept demanding more and more money from the colonies. Eventually, war between Britain and her colonies broke out in 1775.

American Independence

In 1776, the colonies made their Declaration of Independence. This meant they didn't want to be part of the British Empire any more and wanted to rule themselves. Thomas Paine's booklet, *Common Sense* was published in 1776. It supported "government by consent". In other words, it said that governments should be elected by the people, and the rules and laws should be chosen by the people too.

The war ended in 1783 and the new country called itself the United States of America. It was different to all other countries at the time, as it was not governed by kings or queens but ordinary people. The first president of the United States was a military general named George Washington.

The enslavement of Africans did not end in the United States until after a civil war, in 1865. John Adams, who became the second president, and his son, John Quincy Adams, who became the sixth president, were the only two presidents who did not "own" any enslaved people while the system of slavery was still in place.

The Beginning of the End
of the System of Slavery

The slave trade, which Ignatius Sancho fought so hard to end, was abolished in the British Isles in 1807, twenty-seven years after his death.

The actual system of slavery in the West Indies took longer to bring to an end. In 1834, former enslaved people became "apprentices" and were made to work for their masters for at least forty-five hours a week, before they could demand payment. Everyone was so unhappy about this new system that it ended early, on 1 August, 1838. At this time, slavery officially ended in the British Empire, and all former slaves became free.

Ignatius Sancho's Legacy

Ignatius Sancho really was the first Black person in the British Isles to vote in 1774 and again, in 1780. His writing inspired many people. He was friends with many artists and musicians and also wrote music himself. His life showed that Africans were just as clever as Europeans and made many people realize that the system of slavery was wrong.

Not only was Ignatius Sancho the first black Briton to vote, he was also the first black Briton to have his death recorded in the papers. This is what the *Gazetteer* said about him:

"About six yesterday morning died suddenly, Mr Ignatius Sancho, grocer, and tea-dealer, of Charles Street, Westminster, a man whose generosity and benevolence were far beyond his humble station. He was honoured with the friendship of the late Rev Mr Sterne, and several of the literati of these times."

Ignatius Sancho was 51 years old when he died. He had been suffering from a disease called gout which, among other things, made it difficult for him to walk.

For me, it was a real pleasure to find out more about Ignatius Sancho. His letters are very funny (the incident with the goose pie is taken from one of them) and also show how much he cared about his family and friends. He made sure that he did whatever he could to help people close to his heart.

Glossary

Chamber pot A bowl kept under the bed to use as a toilet at night.

Christmas box Servants and suppliers were given small Christmas 'tips' in their Christmas box. This is how Boxing Day got its name.

Coiffeur A hairdresser.

Compensation Money given to someone to recognize loss, suffering or injury.

Dame school A local school for young children, usually run by a woman from her home.

Flogged Beaten with a whip or stick.

Gum arabic Hardened sap from trees used to thicken, stabilize and mix ingredients.

Grotto A natural, or man-made, cave.

Lampblack Very fine black powder that comes from burning oil, tar, resin or fat.

Legacy   An amount of money or property left to someone in a Will.

Literati   Well-read people who are interested in books and culture.

Minuet   A social dance for two people.

Pawnbroker   A shop which lends money in exchange for something of value, which can be sold if the money is not repaid.

Quarry   A place where gravel, sand or chalk is dug out from.

Sampler   A piece of embroidery, which shows off different types of stitches, often containing the alphabet and a motto.

Sedan chair   An enclosed chair for someone to sit inside and get carried about in.

Snuff   Tobacco in powder form, inhaled through the nose or chewed.

Will   A legal document that says what you want to happen after your death.